MOTO-KINESTHETIC
SPEECH TRAINING

MOTO-KINESTHETIC
SPEECH TRAINING

By EDNA HILL YOUNG
and
SARA STINCHFIELD HAWK

STANFORD UNIVERSITY PRESS
STANFORD, CALIFORNIA

Moto-Kinesthetic Speech Training *is based on the book* Children with Delayed or Defective Speech: Motor-Kinesthetic Factors in Their Training, *by Sara M. Stinchfield and Edna Hill Young, first published by Stanford University Press in 1938.*

Stanford University Press
Stanford, California
Copyright 1955 by the Board of Trustees
of the Leland Stanford Junior University
Printed in the United States of America
Original edition 1955
Reprinted 1965

DEDICATED TO ALL TEACHERS
OF SPEECH CORRECTION

FOREWORD

While I was a lecturer during the summer of 1940 at the University of Southern California, I was invited to visit the Hill-Young School of Speech, a residential school for speech-defectives. Here I first observed the effectiveness of what is now called the moto-kinesthetic method of speech correction. Mr. and Mrs. Young had established this school to demonstrate the new methods which Mrs. Young had developed to solve a speech problem in her own life.

With the outbreak of World War II, Mrs. Young came to Denver, where she started a similar school. This school was taken over by the School of Speech at the University of Denver, and has since developed into one of the largest speech clinics for children in the United States. The methods developed by Mrs. Young are at the center of the comprehensive program of clinical services which are now taught in this laboratory.

The modern speech pathologist will find that the moto-kinesthetic methods, like modern drugs for the medical doctor, are indispensable along with his other forms of therapy. Scores of speech correctionists who have mastered these methods have found that there are many cases of speech defect which seem to respond only to these methods; other cases respond with a combination of these methods with different methods. Many cases observed to be at an impasse were speeded up in their therapy with the application of the moto-kinesthetic method, which is no longer in an experimental stage.

Mrs. Young was given an honorary degree of Doctor of Pedagogy in 1944 by Hastings College, Nebraska. She had previously been given an honorary membership into Zeta Phi Eta, National Speech and Arts Fraternity, and she has an honorary life membership as a Fellow of the American Speech and Hearing Association.

Dr. Sara Stinchfield Hawk was one of the first psychologists in the country to undertake the systematic study of speech correction, after study at Columbia University and the state universities of Iowa and Wisconsin. For several years she worked with Mrs. Young in the operation of the Hill-Young school in Los Angeles, where students from the University of Southern California were trained in the method.

Dr. Hawk was formerly Associate Professor of Psychology at Mount Holyoke College, summer Instructor in Psychology and Speech Pathology at Pennsylvania State College, spending her sabbatical in study at the Froeschels Clinic, Vienna, and in London. When she came to California, she became a lecturer at the University of Southern California and visiting Associate Professor at Scripps College and Claremont Graduate School. She is a past President of the American Speech and Hearing Association.

Dr. Hawk has been recently associated with Los Angeles State College, and serves as consultant to several schools and medical centers for handicapped children.

ELWOOD MURRAY

SCHOOL OF SPEECH
UNIVERSITY OF DENVER
January 1955

TABLE OF CONTENTS

*Illustrations for Part One occur between
pages 52 and 53 and for Part Two between
pages 140 and 141*

MOTO-KINESTHETIC
SPEECH TRAINING

Part One

By EDNA HILL YOUNG

INTRODUCTION

The moto-kinesthetic viewpoint regarding speech and the techniques which grew out of it were based upon factual experiences in the life of the writer. A preparation for observation and study was laid from early childhood by the careful training and teaching of the writer's father, who had been educated in New England at a time when the "scientific attitude" was gaining its first foothold. His especial interest lay in education, in better teaching methods, and in a better development of the minds of children and youth.

The West, then opening up, offered opportunities for pioneer educators in its newly settled country. The writer's father went to Columbus, Nebraska, where he entered enthusiastically into the educational program of the new country. However, he was not to influence the beginnings of education there for long. A scourge of diphtheria broke out, causing the death of many, and leaving the writer's father an invalid for many years, unable to continue his vital interest in public education.

The writer mentions these facts because, her father's interest in public education having been thwarted, his attention was turned to the teaching of his children. His emphasis lay always in fact finding, in nature around them, in the relationship of the heavenly bodies to the earth at various seasons, in building up number concepts by handling objects, and by having his children create their own rules in arithmetic, instead of merely learning rules from the book. He created projects for their study, from the observation of which his children early learned that what appears on first observation is not always the correct answer. The writer emphasizes this training, because a habit of careful observation and study of details was thus formed, which later led to the years of study of the facts which were a part of her own experience in speech. At about the age of fifteen years she became increasingly aware of a difficulty connected with her own speech. (The details of the writer's experience are given in the chapter on "Stuttering.")

During the next twenty years, while doing the work of a regular teacher in the public schools, the writer experimented with pupils who had defective speech and who wanted help. She finally came to the conclusion that there was something basic and vital in the help which her developing method offered. Acting upon this conclusion, she decided to spend the rest of her life in demonstrating this very realistic approach to the development of normal speech and to speech correction.

The writer and her husband, George Kelson Young, united in starting the "Hill-Young School of Speech" in 1923, in which resident speech-defectives were maintained to demonstrate the use of the "Hill-Young"—

3

later named "moto-kinesthetic"—methods. This school operated for five years in Minneapolis and for thirteen years in Los Angeles.

In 1938, Dr. Sara M. Stinchfield Hawk and the writer wrote the book, *Children with Delayed or Defective Speech*.[1] Dr. Stinchfield Hawk observed and did research on the methods used at the Hill-Young school during a five-year period. One part of this 1938 book is a report of Dr. Stinchfield Hawk's research. Another is a description of the techniques used in the moto-kinesthetic work, as described by this writer.

From 1936 to 1942, Dr. Stinchfield Hawk and the writer jointly conducted a class through the Extension Department of the University of Southern California under Dean Ray K. Immel, in which Dr. Stinchfield Hawk gave students the background and techniques of speech correction as taught generally at that period. The writer taught the techniques of the moto-kinesthetic method, and used the pupils of the Hill-Young School to demonstrate these techniques. Students preparing to become teachers of speech correction were given credit for this course by the University. As World War II came on, and it seemed inadvisable to continue the residential school in the coastal area, the writer went to Denver, and organized a Children's Clinic at the University of Denver under Dr. Elwood Murray, where she continued the work along the same line as in Los Angeles. Resident work was again established, and teacher-training in the use of all techniques, including the moto-kinesthetic.

In closing this introduction, the writer wishes to express her great and lasting appreciation of her husband's untiring part in their mutual effort. Also, especial appreciation to the following persons: Dr. Ray K. Immel, formerly of the University of Southern California Speech Department, through whose interest and encouragement the Hill-Young School of Speech was moved from Minneapolis to Los Angeles; and to Dr. Sara Stinchfield Hawk, Dr. Lee Edward Travis, Dr. Eugene Hahn, deceased, and Dr. Paul Pfaff, who were members of a committee at the time of the Rockefeller grant, and who started research on the moto-kinesthetic methods and techniques. World War II stopped all research in this direction, as members of the committee were called into government service and scattered.

Grateful appreciation is extended to the officials of the University of Denver, especially to Dean A. C. Nelson, Dean Edward J. Allen, and to Dr. Elwood Murray and Dr. Ruth M. Clark of the School of Speech, for their backing and constant support of the work at Denver.

Appreciation is also extended to the following persons from the University of Denver, who assisted the writer in 1951, in making a moving picture of the techniques of the moto-kinesthetic method, available now through the University of Denver: Ruth Van Tine, R. Edwin Shutts, Richard Woellhof, and Richard Winchester.

[1] S. M. Stinchfield and E. H. Young, *Children with Delayed or Defective Speech* (Stanford, Calif.: Stanford University Press, 1938).

CHAPTER ONE

THE AIR CURRENT AS THE BASIS OF SPEECH

An understanding of the part which the air current plays in speech is fundamental for one who is to direct the speech processes through the moto-kinesthetic method. Therefore we start our study with the realization of the various uses of the air which makes speech possible. The definite co-ordination of muscular movements, which are vital to the production of each usage, and the stimulations which tend to produce them will be discussed in later chapters.

Perhaps the student, in beginning this study, might start by thinking of different ways outside of the human mechanism in which he has known air to be used, in producing sound effects. He has perhaps heard the wind blowing through cracks or openings in old buildings. He has doubtless pressed the bulb of a hand syringe, and heard the escape of air at the opening. Does it not remind one of the sound represented by the letter *h*? Place a finger over the circular opening of the outlet tube, almost but not fully covering it, and squeeze the bulb again. Here is a sound more like the sound of *f*. Now place a finger firmly over the entire opening, squeeze the bulb, then pull the finger away quickly from the opening. This sound is similar in production to *p*, *t*, or *k*. Place a vibrating tuning fork over containers of different shapes. The change in resonance is illustrative of the sounds of speech such as the vowels, for each of which a chamber of definite shape is required for resonance, and through which the air current may pass. Whatever the sound or sounds used in speech, the basis of production is the air current, as it is acted upon in very definite ways to produce the sounds of speech.

There is just as definite a use of the air current in speech as it moves from sound to sound, as there is in the production of sounds in the wind instruments. As one watches the players of these instruments in the orchestra, it is very evident that the constant use of a current of air is essential to the production of these kinds of musical sounds. It is evident also that the use of the air current is constantly changed inside the instrument, by the application of the player's fingers to the different keys.

The use of the air current in the human instrument is not so obvious. The many changing uses of the air current in speech give no visible clues to the observer as to what is happening to the current in order to produce the changes in sound. What is seen by the observer, as he watches speech, is the changing movements of the jaw, the tongue, and the lips. It is not strange then, that the emphasis has too often been focused upon the parts seen to move, as the speech sound is made. One cannot see the air as it is being acted upon by the muscles of speech and as it is being made to perform a succession of uses, while the current passes outward through the pharynx, the mouth, or the nose. He cannot see the source of the air current. The person who would help find the way to produce the sounds of speech from the human mechanism is greatly aided by getting a clear mental picture of the various possible ways in which air may be used for sound production. If it were possible to visualize the uses of the air, the task would be much simpler.

The writer has felt that a cartoon of the Disney variety might be worked out to advantage, to clarify the uses of the air current in speech. The action of the muscles should be shown, but along with the muscular activity, the use to which the air is being subjected could be shown in color at the place of its use. For instance, the part of the current to be used for the first sound of the word might be pictured as green, the next use as yellow, etc. Lines or dots passing through the colored part could indicate the manner of use to which the air is being subjected at a given point. This might be done in slow motion as first observed, but should later be shown in normal timing.

Let us illustrate the use of the cartoon with the word "pig," starting the word in the cartoon from a closed mouth position. The jaw with the lower lip would be shown to move downward as in normal speech. However, unlike normal speech, the air would be shown as colored, moving outward immediately as the lips part in completing the *p*. By that time, the mouth would have reshaped itself for the vowel. A steady movement of the air as required for the vowel, accompanied by vibrations, might be shown in one constant color at the larynx, wherever voice is required in the cartoon. The last sound, *g*, could show muscular action closing off the air by lifting the back of the tongue. The use of some sort of symbol might show the air as checked back of that closure. Voice color might show that the vibrations are in use, while the air is thus checked. Immediately, the back of the tongue should be shown coming down. The same color as was used back of the closure should be used to indicate the escape of the air as it first moves over the back of the tongue, as the back moves downward. The whole word could in this way be shown as produced by a sequence of muscular processes, with the effect of each process simultaneously shown upon the air current. The moving picture suggested here would enable the student to form better mental pictures of the uses of the air current as a basis for speech. The use to which the air current is to be subjected at any given point makes it imperative for muscular action of a definite kind to come at that point, and to act upon the current in the required way. As languages have been evolved, the sequence of sounds, which name a given object in any language, determines the sequence of muscular movements to be stimulated to produce these changing sounds throughout a given word.

It is important for the teacher of speech correction to be able to visualize the whole process of speech production, as the mechanic visualizes in advance the workings of the complicated machine which he is about to install. If the student of speech starts with the visualization of the moving of the air current, he may add to this picture, step by step, the visualization of the total processes involved when any sentence is spoken. The mechanism, which furnishes an air current for speech purposes, makes use of the natural mechanism by which air is taken into the lungs, in breathing, and is then discarded, along with impurities. It is this discarded air current which has been turned into use for normal speech. As the discarded air is being moved upward to eliminate it from the body, a "squeeze action" against the air container, the lungs, is taking place, to force the impure air out of the lungs. When the squeeze action has almost completed its task of removal of the used air, a reversal of the process takes place. The diaphragm, which has been forced upward by the contraction of muscles in the upper abdomen, now moves downward. The ribs, which have been moving inward against the lungs, through the control of muscular activity, now move outward. Co-ordinating muscular activity relaxes, and more space is created within the lungs. This enlargement of the space, in which the residual air is contained, rarefies the air and causes an immediate downward movement of air into the lungs from the outside to equalize the air pressure, thus filling them again. To the primary, physiological uses of the air, the complicated functioning for speech production was added as languages evolved. The factors controlling the primary uses are unchanged; however, slight variations are introduced by the production of speech. As the outgoing current is used in daily speech, the length of time for its emission is extended beyond the normal time used in breathing. This extended period of time in emission furnishes the necessary basis for the production of longer sentences for the expression of thought. Also, the length of time for the intake of air becomes shorter than in normal breathing, in order that sentences may follow each other without delay. Another change in the primary uses is seen in the quick intake of air through the mouth for speech; the air is normally drawn through the nostrils, in ordinary breathing. The normal intake of air in speech is done in whatever position the mouth happens to be, when the new intake is needed. No additional moving of the lips is necessary for the intake, unless they are closed as for *m*, or partially closed as for *f*. The concentration should be on taking the air quickly through the mouth, although there is simultaneously some movement of air through the nose.

As a basis for the better understanding of speech production, a student is helped by visualizing as fully as possible the make-up of the air. Such a picture enables one to think of the air as made up of real entities, the molecules, which are capable of transmitting force in all directions from the place of origin of that force. Apply this fact to the movement of air in speech. When the co-ordinated activity of the muscles from below starts the air upward to be discarded, the force created by this combined activity of muscles first acts upon the lower layers of molecules in the lungs,

which in turn pass on an equal energy throughout the whole column, starting the molecules at the lips or nostrils outward. These are followed immediately by layer upon layer of molecules in quick succession under constant pressure from below. Thus a current is formed, made up of moving
air particles. These air particles may act with more or less force, according
to the amount of force which is applied to them from below. Now carry the
picture a little farther. This moving air column, intended originally for dis-
card, is moved through a continuous passageway where, as it passes
through the upper part of its journey, it may be acted upon in a great variety of ways, each producing a different sound, according to the laws of
sound production. It helps to clarify speech to visualize the moving current
as it is acted upon in each definite way. Try to imagine the molecules acting
in response to each co-ordinated muscular process. Think of them as
forced out at the lips, as the sound of *p* is made. Think of them in each
use as described later on, and imagine them, after each use, as followed
by the oncoming mass of molecules—with no break in continuity, and no
intervening vacuum. Visualize the molecules of the air used in speech
as real, though unseen particles, and then try to visualize each activity of
muscles upon these real entities. Pressue against the lungs created by a
co-ordination of muscular movements may be pictured as having the same
effect inwardly as the tightening of a belt outside, around the waistline.
The effect of this tightening action is seen outwardly, as one watches the
action of the front walls of the body from side to side. These walls move
inward, as if to some common center during the emission of air for speech.
One effective stimulation for the correct use of the air current during
speech is to tie a thick cord or soft rope around the waist, in a loose
single knot. Direct the subject to draw air through the lips, as is done in
normal speech. The cord is fitted around the waist line. The subject can
see it expand as he takes in the air. Immediately upon the intake, tighten
the knot gradually while the subject moves the air outward through the
mouth, or projects sound. Let him practice vowel sounds, that he may
become aware of the possible steady inward movement brought about by
muscular control. Then the practice of sounds *ha, ka, ta, pa* (*a* as in *arm*)
about four times, with one emission of the air current, will lead him to
feel the action of the diaphragm and co-ordinating muscles, which are
capable of sending sound outward with force. The student should realize
that the general movement of the surrounding walls is inward, as long as
he is talking, with one emission of the air current. When practicing *ha*,
some students are apt to take a new breath between the syllables. This
exercise should be done with one intake of air, each syllable bringing
the enclosing walls closer to the center. The closing position of one *ha* is
the starting point of the next—four definite inward movements, each requiring that the surrounding walls press further inward.

It will be noted then that the steady pressure of the controlling muscles, to bring the air upward, is only one phase of this picture of air con-

trol. It is more complicated than that. Some sounds need more pressure from below than do others. Some sounds are made by forcing the air through two parts which are in contact, as in the sound of *f*. Firm, steady pressure is used for such sounds. The sound represented by *h* requires a comparatively large volume of air to be moved upward, and it must come through the passageway with force and speed, or the amount of friction produced will not be sufficient to make the sound satisfactorily. The vowels, on the other hand, use the air economically and thus help to produce more words in one emission of the air current than would otherwise be the case.

There are a few sounds which seem to the writer, after long experimentation, to bring about sound effects from the human mechanism as the result of some sort of conflict or friction among the air particles themselves, when forced suddenly to make an adjustment to a new pathway. Such changes in sound are heard and recognized only as one directs the air current through direct stimulation, in mouths of subjects who have not previously made them. The teacher by direct stimulation changes the course of the air current, as it starts to flow through a definitely shaped chamber or outlet into another shape or opening while the vocal cords are still vibrating. It is just at this point of quick change in usage that a change in sound effect is brought about. (See Chapter Five, stimulations for *r*, *l*, *w*, and *y*.) Some other sound effects used in speech seem to result from a current of air under pressure being sent suddenly against a mass of comparatively static molecules. It would look as if the sudden impact and quick readjustment of molecules in this fluid turmoil might be responsible for these sounds. (See *p*, *t*, and *k*, in Chapter Three.)

We have taken up the thought of the air current first, because in the production of speech, the kind of uses of the air is always an essential part of the picture, first in one way, then in another. The movements which we see, as we watch another person talk, are the means used to bring about certain usages of the air current, changing from sound to sound. In other words, the air current is constantly being acted upon. Something is done to it. A sound is produced. A certain something is done to the next consecutive part of the current, another sound comes forth, and so on, until it is time to take in another supply of air to be acted upon in a similar manner.

What is done to the current with each sound production is the work of the muscles which are concerned with the making of that sound. Let us call the total effort in action, in tensions, or in co-ordinated effort with other muscles which go into the making of one sound a "process." Each process is a unit in itself, but each unit process must be completed and the mouth muscles must move into the next unit process in the most direct way possible, to produce an easy flow of movements and to permit sound to follow sound with ease, without a break in the word sequences.

The emphasis so far has been placed on the air current as a basis for the study of speech. Now our study must relate the thought of the air current to the muscles which are capable of using it in definite ways and changing it into a large variety of sound sequences, as languages have evolved.

Chapter Two develops the thought of a method, the moto-kinesthetic, by which the teacher visualizes the use to which the air current is to be put for each sound and, by direct stimulation, helps the muscular activity normally involved to function correctly. The aim of this method is to prevent some of the incorrect learning which is common in the beginnings of speech, and to help in the correction of speech. The stimulations are definite, and they aid in practical usage, in a large majority of cases where changes in movements are involved. In the use of this method, another sense, the kinesthetic, is added as well as the tactile, to the use of the visual and the auditory, thus associating the idea, the visual concept, the sound, and the feeling of the movements in sequence, all in one learning process.

CHAPTER TWO

INTRODUCTION
TO THE MOTO-KINESTHETIC METHOD

When considering the moto-kinesthetic viewpoint and techniques, the psychological aspects of speech and their relationship to speech training are not minimized or ignored. Moto-kinesthetic speech training is much more than the manipulation of muscles. As in other approaches to the speech problem, the whole child is considered first. In fact, the manipulation of muscles should rarely be attempted in the first contacts of teacher and patient. Whatever period of time is necessary should be allowed for getting acquainted, leading gradually to the thought of speech. Without the correct approach psychologically, the manipulations may fail, but without added help through the manipulations, psychology cannot do alone, in many cases, what the combined therapies can do together, when used as an integrated whole, relatively adjusted to each other and to the individual patient. The teacher should be prepared to use all available aids before she undertakes the actual training.

Through training in the use of the moto-kinesthetic techniques, a teacher is enabled to direct muscular activity as a guide to the subject's learning. There is a norm for each sound production, also a standard stimulation which tends to produce each norm. In the beginning study of the stimulations for various sounds (see Chapters Three, Four, and Five), let us consider the subject to be one who has normal auditory, kinesthetic, visual, and tactile sensibility. The loss or variation in one or more of these senses requires certain adjustments to compensate for each kind of loss, but the standard stimulations are fundamental and should be learned first. After the teacher has learned the standard stimulations through observation, study, and practice, the next step is to learn to adjust these fundamental techniques to the various classifications of speech defects and then to the individuals in each group where there are deviations from the normal conditions.

Muscular Activity as Related to the Air Current in Speech

In the analysis of the mechanics of speech, the changing uses of the air current remain fundamental. The order of uses changes from language to language. A child generally learns the language to which he is exposed. He learns the sequence of sounds which stand for objects or ideas in the language of those around him. A certain action or several co-ordinated actions of muscles upon the air current in the upper passageways cause a sound to be made in one part. As soon as the process required to make one use of the air current is completed, these muscles are relaxed while another co-ordinated group of muscles has become ready to continue action

11

upon the air current, and a continuity of processes is thus made possible, producing a continuity of sound. The learning involved requires a definite co-ordination of muscular activities not only of the muscles used in speech and the muscles which control the air current, but also the co-ordination of speech muscles with other muscles involved in facial expression. The task is a tremendous one. Some children easily gain the normal functioning of muscles which is necessary to bring about the flow of sounds required in correct speech. Others are not so fortunate. There is a wide range of difference in the way in which children acquire the use of their speech muscles. Beginning at the lower levels of attainment, there are some who are speechless. There are others who but partially master the problem and who make great effort to talk, but are understood with difficulty. Between these groups and the higher levels of attainment there are a great many gradations in the use of the muscles of speech.

In cases where there is a delay in speech development, or where learning has been incorrect, real help is possible to speech development through the guidance and direction of speech muscles by a carefully trained adult. This method of definite stimulation to speech muscles has been called the "moto-kinesthetic method of speech training."

Let us consider the meaning of the stimulations used in this method. The child's big task in learning or in correcting speech is to find the way to move his mouth in order to make sounds correctly. Since a co-ordination of movements is always a part of the task, the teacher's help is directed toward bringing about co-ordination of as many of the parts as possible. For instance, there is always the outside visible action to consider, as well as the unseen movements of the muscles used in speech. Lips may take part in a particular sound or, if not, they are often moved to the corners to clear the pathway for some sound moving outward from within. Sometimes the teacher can give only a partial stimulation—but even a partial stimulation helps.

Some sounds require frontal tongue action, others back-of-tongue action. The sensing of how to start action, at the front or the back, is stimulated by the teacher's touch or pressure at either part. (More detailed directions will be given later on.) When the part to be moved is located, the next question is, "In what *direction* is the movement to be made?" The teacher sets the pattern not only for the location of the movement, but also stimulates the direction and form of the movement needed. Thus location of the muscular functioning is stimulated and also, at the same time, the feeling of the direction of movement. A certain degree of pressure of one part against another is sometimes needed. The degree of pressure may be stimulated as well as the timing, and all of these factors may be felt simultaneously through the stimulation of the teacher's fingers.

One kind of stimulation actually moves the part involved, thus setting a pattern for the movement to be learned. When the child feels the movement or movements, it is easy to reproduce the pattern, through the kinesthetic sense. The feel of what happens "stays" in the muscles, becoming associated with the auditory patterns as the teacher speaks the word. An illustration of this kind of stimulation is seen when the teacher moves the lower lip upward, adjusting it to the upper teeth, preparatory to the emission of air for the sound of *f*.

Another illustration is the definite stimulation of the movements of the jaw, as directed by the teacher. Each sound is aided by the teacher's guidance of the lower jaw, since variations for different sounds occur in the relative size of the opening of the mouth. Pressure on the bridge of the nose tends to send sound through the nasal chambers, when that is desired.

A stimulation which influences the tip of the tongue to move forward, and to act against the dental ridge, is the firm pressure of the teacher's finger against the same location on the outside. If *t* (as in "Tom") is sought, pressure on the mid-line outside, above the upper lip tends to bring the tongue end inside toward the point of pressure. A quick action of the teacher's finger downward from the first position is felt through the tactile sense, and may also serve as a visual aid to bring the tongue end quickly downward for the emission of air in the front location.

The degree of pressure used by the teacher in a stimulation tends to call forth a like degree of pressure in response. Timing as used by the teacher's stimulation also tends to bring like timing in the child's response. The direction of the movement desired is sensed by the child as the teacher's fingers move over the surface in the direction which is required for certain sounds. Likewise, some of these stimulations used by the teacher on herself, not touching the child, serve as a visual stimulation to show him where to move and how to do it.

All of these stimulations are for the purpose of guiding the muscular processes which in turn act upon the air current so as to produce sounds. The teacher says the word simultaneously as she gives the stimulation. The auditory pattern becomes associated with the feel of the sequence of movements. Thus a word is gained, and is associated with the idea in the brain. Before the brain has become able to direct muscular activity to the correct muscles in the peripheral area for the expression of thought or emotion, the learning process may actually be directed by the teacher and started in these areas, to be used by the brain afterward as a means of expression. The learning is done with greater accuracy by being directed. Skill on the teacher's part is the basis for satisfactory results in the use of the moto-kinesthetic techniques. The child has the capacity for responding to this kind of teaching, but the patterns stimulated must be the correct ones.

The typist's skill in the use of her fingers is illustrative of the skill which should be acquired by the teacher in the art of producing effective stimulations for speech activity. A training period, under someone who has already acquired the necessary skill, hastens the learning, in the same way that the beginning typist is aided through a course of training. Likewise, the speech therapist who gains the skill to move the fingers from part to part, touching with accurate pressure, definitely giving the feeling of direction of movement to the subject, is in a position to use the moto-kinesthetic techniques automatically, and is then free to give her whole attention to the training process, and to the whole child.

CHAPTER THREE

THE VOICELESS CONSONANTS

The voiceless consonants are those which are produced by various uses of the air current as brought about through definite muscular activity without the action of the vocal folds. They are represented by the following symbols:

VOICELESS CONSONANTS

Webster's Dictionary	International Phonetic Alphabet*
h	h
wh	ʍ
f	f
th	θ
p	p
t	t
k	k
s	s
sh	ʃ
ch	tʃ

* G. W. Gray and C. M. Wise, *The Bases of Speech* (New York: Harper & Brothers, 1946).

STIMULATION FOR THE SOUND OF *h*

As the current of air in the human mechanism moves against surrounding parts or walls on its outward pathway, friction is produced and is audible. This simple sound is utilized as one element with which to build speech, and is represented by the letter *h*. If the trainer makes the sound and the child is unable to repeat it, she may place one hand at the child's waistline over the diaphragm, pressing inward and upward while the other hand moves the child's jaw to a lowered position. The sound of escaping air is the result sought. Since the method described does not stop with the production of one sound, the trainer quickly moves the child's mouth into the position for the sound following, usually a vowel. In the first work on *h*, it is simpler to practice with the same vowel following the *h*. The short *a* as in "hat" is good to begin with, because the teacher's hold on the lower jaw for *h* is close to that used to start the stimulation for the short *a*. (See Chapter Four.)

When the child is led gradually, step by step, to adjust to this form of speech training, the time will come when he will be willing to assume a reclining position during short periods. In the reclining position, he is more completely relaxed, and can sense the stimulations for speech more completely than in the upright position. The teacher is aided in stimu-

15

lating the sounds by eliminating the usual head and body movements which are apt to occur in the child's upright position.

For the stimulation of *ha* as in "hat," when the child is in a reclining position, the teacher, if right-handed, may find it simpler to cross hands using her right hand to move the jaw, while her left land brings inward and upward pressure at the waistline to control the air current. After *ha* is spoken normally, other vowels may be practiced following the *h* sound. (See Chapter Four for vowel stimulations.)

STIMULATION FOR THE SOUND OF *wh*

The use of the air current in the stimulation for *wh* is very similar to that for *h*; the quick forceful expulsion of air is the same. The difference lies in the nature of the outer opening through which the air is passed. The trainer moves the lips from the corners toward the mid-line, forming a rounded or elongated opening. She may do this with her preferential hand and, with the other hand at the waistline, she presses inward and upward as she does for the stimulation of the *h* sound. The air is thus forced quickly upward, and out through the central opening at the lips, to produce the *wh* sound. The blowing sound resulting from the forced movement of air through the narrowed opening causes a variation in sound from that of the *h*, which has an open mouth as an outlet to the air. As soon as the movement of air through the opening is heard (the *wh* sound), the trainer moves the mouth into the position for the vowel to follow, with no break in sound.

STIMULATION FOR THE SOUND OF *f*

For the *f* sound, the trainer moves the lower lip upward until it comes in contact with the curved edge of the upper teeth. Just as the contact is made, she gives the auditory stimulation herself. Simultaneously with the other hand she presses inward and upward at the waistline, causing the air to pass between the upper teeth and the lower lip as held in contact. As soon as the sound is heard sufficiently, the trainer moves the lip downward, and into the next sound position.

A lip which has not habitually passed through this upward movement, when attempting the *f* sound, may present an appearance of being too wide from corner to corner to fit the curve of the upper teeth. Massaging it gently from the corners toward the mid-line tends to shorten the lip. Training the lip upward, getting the "feel" of the correct contact of lip against the upper teeth, gradually makes it possible for the subject to direct his own movement without the manual directive.

The adjustment of lower lip to the upper teeth for *f* (or *v*) is influenced by the nature of the child's occlusion. If the "bite" is normal, the lower lip very easily adjusts, since the lower teeth move upward slightly back of the upper teeth, bringing the lower lip close to the upper incisors. If the "bite" is that of an undershot jaw, the lower lip and teeth protruding outside the line of the upper teeth, the adjustment is more difficult. The lower lip in that case moves upward and over the lower front teeth and then contacts the upper teeth—sometimes a difficult learning process. The difficulty is greatly reduced, however, through the teacher's help in finding the best adjustment for the individual case. The outer, colored portion of the lips should show. If possible, the line of demarcation between the lining of the mouth and the outside of the lower lip should be the line of contact between the lower lip and the upper teeth. The appearance of the mouth is aided by a slight moving of the lips toward the corners, as the lower lip learns to adjust to the upper teeth for *f* or *v*.

STIMULATION FOR THE SOUND OF VOICELESS *th*

For the sound of *th* as in "think," the trainer directs the tongue end forward and upward until contact is made with the edge of the upper incisors. The air is now forced between this edge and the tongue as it adjusts to the teeth. The aim of the trainer should be to teach the tongue to lift until the borders find the curved line represented by the edges of the upper teeth. Sometimes it is necessary to place the tongue (by the use of a tongue depressor) against the edge of the upper teeth, permitting the child to feel and to become used to this curved edge, as the end or limit of the tongue's movement. The blade of the tongue needs to be broadened out somewhat, and to lift from whatever position it may be in, with the curved edge of the upper teeth as its objective. As soon as the escaping air is heard, the trainer may move the tongue depressor quickly away from the tongue, into the first movement required for the next sound. The child's incorrect habit may be in moving the tongue against the dental ridge, instead of the edges of the teeth. This results in the sound of "tink" instead of "think."

The next three sounds—symbolized by *p*, *t*, and *k*—are produced by the trainer's stimulation of the air current, with a temporary closing of the passageway, then opening it suddenly to emit a puff of air. This closing off of the air current is possible in three different locations: (1) at the lips, (2) with the front of the tongue in contact with the dental ridge, or (3) with the back of the tongue as it contacts the soft palate.

STIMULATION FOR THE SOUND OF *p*

To produce the *p* sound, place the thumb and forefinger on the lower jaw, below the lower lip, moving it upward until it presses against the upper lip. Without lifting the hand from contact with the lower jaw, bring the lower lip and jaw downward, quickly and firmly, usually securing the "puff" of air as the lower lip is made to part from the upper. If she does not succeed in getting the *p* sound, the teacher may place her hand at the child's waistline, moving it inward with a quick gentle movement just as her other hand brings the jaw downward, and so causing the air to escape quickly. In directing the movement for the *p* sound, it is important, for the best habit formation, not to touch the upper lip with the hand. The two steps are: (1) to move the lower jaw and lip upward until a firm contact with the upper lip is made, and (2) to reverse the movement and proceed downward and into the next sound process.

STIMULATION FOR THE SOUND OF *t*

To stimulate the *t* sound, the end of the tongue is brought upward in contact with the dental ridge, to permit the tongue to close off the current of air temporarily. Usually the depressor, inserted under the tongue and bringing it by a quick upward movement to the dental ridge, brings about the necessary contact. The depressor is then brought down quickly, releasing the tongue and thus giving it the suggestion of a rapid downward action. The air is released as the tongue is released, making the sound represented by the letter *t*. The child may be led into the simple suggestion of a tongue-end movement by the trainer's touching the center of the region outside and above the upper lip and quickly bringing the finger downward. This external suggestion is often sufficient. The touch above the lip, outside the dental ridge, suggests that the tongue tip move upward inside, opposite the point touched, then quickly down as the finger moves down. It is often wise to try this outside stimulation first, especially with a child who resents the use of the tongue depressor. It is not necessary to open the mouth wide when the teacher uses this outside stimulation. The outer appearance should be that of normal speech.

STIMULATION FOR THE SOUND OF *k*

To produce the *k* sound, in difficult cases, the tongue depressor may be placed on the tip of the tongue, holding it down, and at the same time pushing the tongue backward and upward until it comes into contact with the soft palate. Immediately, the tongue depressor draws the tongue downward and forward, opening the closure, thus enabling the air to move outward. The suggestion of the movement by the trainer's hands, on the outside, tends to produce the sound. Place the thumb on one side of the throat, under the back of the tongue externally, and the index finger on the opposite side. Press upward, thus suggesting that the back of the tongue move upward then move downward quickly, thus suggesting a quick downward movement to the back of the tongue, in order to allow the sudden escape of air for the *k* sound. The child may be accustomed to start movement at the end of the tongue, thus producing a *t* beginning instead of *k*.

THE APPROACH TO THE SOUND OF *s*

There are many problems connected with the production of a satisfactory *s* in speech, but these can be minimized by observing certain fundamentals. Whatever the nature of the physical conditions presented, the first step is a study of the particular case to find out how to bring about a small enclosed passageway through which the air may be forced under pressure from below. Imagine the mid-line channel at the front of the tongue as the lower part of the passageway, and picture the two sides of the tongue, extending from the mid-line channel up to the line of contact with the dental ridge, as the sides of the passageway sought, while the part of the dental ridge enclosed by those two sides may form the upper part of the passageway. Thus, we have, in imagination, constructed a small tunnel through which the air may be forced outward from below.

STIMULATION FOR THE SOUND OF *s*

There are several definite steps by which we may realize the conditions imagined above. The first step in the stimulation of the *s* sound is for the trainer to bring the child's lower jaw straight upward as in natural closing. The molars are thus brought together naturally, without pressure. The joints controlling the lower jaw are thus permitted to function normally—a very important factor in securing greatest ease and skill in the use of the muscles of speech.

ADJUSTMENT OF JAWS IN THE NORMAL OCCLUSION

Where the occlusion is normal, the lower incisors should pass up a little behind the upper ones, as the sounds of *s, sh, ch,* and *j* come in speech. The molars all but occlude. With this form of occlusion (see Fig. 10) the greatest freedom of movement possible is effected for speech. The joints thus function normally, and the edge of the lower incisors cannot interfere with the upper ones because they bypass them in closing. There is a natural way out for the air current between the incisors, as they adjust in the case of the normal occlusion.

However, there are many cases in which the person with normal occlusion fails to realize his best functioning. Some push the lower jaw outward, bringing the edges of the incisors together, in the appearance of the end-to-end "bite." These people fail to find the ease which a simple straight up-and-down functioning gives, since an unnecessarily forward movement adds to the complexity of the speech process.

One such case, a little girl of ten years, will illustrate this form of unsatisfactory habit of speech. The occlusion was normal. The habit, in which the lower jaw protruded outward, had been formed early in life. The lower incisors even moved up outside the upper ones as the *s* came in speech. The appearance of the mouth was unsightly. The functioning was obstructive and difficult. It was a delighted little girl who found that it was not necessary to continue this uncomfortable, unsightly form of jaw action. Her mouth was capable of the normal movements. It was not undershot by nature, but had such an appearance through acquired habit.

The end-to-end "bite."—Where the joints are functioning naturally, and the incisors come together in the end-to-end "bite," care must be observed that enough space is left between the two rows of incisors for the outward passage of the air as it leaves the mid-line depression. There are cases which fail to find a satisfactory *s* sound because the incisors habitually block off the air by too tight a closure. One such case found success immediately on the very slight parting of the two rows of incisors, thus gaining the necessary outlet for the air current after leaving the mid-line passageway over the tongue. Care must also be taken not to leave too wide a space between the edges of the two rows of incisors. A teacher should experiment to find the exact opening needed, and then help the subject to practice this form until it becomes habitual.

The undershot jaw.—If the normal functioning of the joints brings the lower incisors outside the upper ones as the jaw closes, the case is that of the undershot jaw. The direct approach to produce the *s* sound is the same as in the other forms of occlusion. This means to find a passageway for the air current which meets the requirements as formerly described. There may be these adjustments necessary: (1) the sides of the tongue may need to fit more closely along the sides of the front of the dental ridge and then to the inside of the upper incisors, or (2) if the passageway for the air current is along the mid-line of the tongue, the lower teeth may need to be placed more carefully in relation to the upper ones, so that the lower incisors may not block the pathway of the outgoing current. In this latter form of occlusion, the end of the tongue usually dips behind the lower incisors, forming a V-shape as it dips.

THE REFINING OF THE GROSSER MOVEMENTS FOR THE *s*

After the stimulations of the grosser movements which form the first steps in the *s* production, there may be a refinement of details necessary, in order to make a sharpened hissing sound. On the other hand, there are cases in which the necessary conditions are fulfilled as soon as the jaws are adjusted in closing. The teacher's auditory pattern may bring the desired sound immediately.

If the attempted *s* sound is too "breathy," the mid-line passageway may be too large or there may be a leak somewhere along the side walls, where every point of the line of contact needs to hold fast to the dental ridge. To ensure close contact of the sides to the dental ridge, the teacher may press outside on either side of the mid-line of the upper jaw. This outside pressure tends to bring the sides of the tongue upward against the dental ridge. Another help, where there is leakage of the air, is to insert a tongue depressor between the two rows of teeth at the sides, actually pressing the sides of the tongue upward against the dental ridge.

A part of the refining process may require work on the mid-line depression. This channel may need a very slight enlarging or a decrease in size. To bring about the enlargement, press at the central line length-wise with the thin edge of the tongue depressor, drawing it along the mid-line to the front between the two halves of the tongue. Then close the jaws again, giving the auditory pattern. To decrease the size of the mid-line channel, press closer to the mid-line channel outside the upper jaw. Also check to see that the outlet between the incisors has been nar-rowed sufficiently vertically to control the size of the outlet. The stimula-tion and training of these finer movements, where they fail at first, bring results in time.

A balanced functioning for s.—In completing the thought of the teacher's stimulations for the *s* sound, there is the thought of balanced functioning to be kept in mind. The appearance of the mouth should be the same on both sides of the mid-line. The central lengthwise depression should coincide with the mid-line of the body. The lips should be drawn equally toward the corners, away from the mid-line, leaving the central space clear for the emission of the air current.

STIMULATION FOR THE SOUND OF *sh*

For the *sh* sound, the subject's jaw is first moved straight up as for the *s* sound. The trainer then places thumb and forefinger outside the upper jaw, starting at the corners, pressing against the upper jaw and at the same time moving the lips somewhat toward the center, protruding slightly, and also indicating by the degree of pressure on the outside, the necessary amount of pressure required to bring the tongue blade up against the dental ridge. The tongue blade is stimulated upward along the whole front surface, as the air comes outward, over the entire surface, not channeled along the mid-line as for *s*.

STIMULATION FOR THE SOUND OF *ch*

To produce the sound of *ch*, the tongue blade is stimulated to form contact with the dental ridge, the same as for *sh*. The outward movement of the lips is the same as for *sh*. After the jaw has been moved into a closed position, the same as for *sh*, the stimulation outside the upper jaw, starting at the corners, and moving toward the mid-line is firmer than for *sh*. Next, the trainer breaks this position by moving the jaw firmly but slightly downward with one hand, and simultaneously removes the other hand from the upper jaw. A sudden release of the air current comes, as the tongue is drawn away from the dental ridge, in unison with the action of the jaw.

CHAPTER FOUR

THE VOWELS

Let us now consider the stimulations which tend to produce the vowel sounds, with the idea that the student may now begin to practice the stimulations for a combination of sounds. Until the method of stimulating vowels is understood, there can be no sequences to work upon.

Perhaps the most fundamental and practical value of the moto-kinesthetic method is its aid in producing a normal sequence of sounds, as found in any monosyllable, instead of sounds attempted separately, leaving the subject to fill in the rest of the sequence, and to find by "trial and error" how to move from one sound into the next. For instance, a child who is saying "thee" for "see" may find how to make the *s* sound alone. That does not mean that there will be an easy transition from "thee" into "see."

In describing the stimulations which lead to the vowel sounds, the outside stimulations are employed first, because they usually work, through repetition of the stimulation. One should not be discouraged if results do not come with the first efforts. Muscles, which are functioning through the force of habit, tend to continue those habits in spite of the stimulations. Also, the stimulations must be well learned by the teacher, through careful study, practice, and experience, before she can achieve the best results. The main concentration, at first, needs to be on the training of her fingers, for they must be ready to move definitely, and in good timing. It helps for two students to practice together on each other, as the techniques are being learned.

To begin with, let us revisualize the air current—it is the foundation for vowel production. See the current moving steadily upward from below and, as it passes through the vocal folds, the vibrations are added to this steady current. For these sounds, an air chamber is formed each time by the action of muscles, so that at the exact moment when the vowel is to be produced in the sequence, the air space must be ready. The air chambers are of various shapes, each shape producing a different sound. After the required shape is made, we may forget the muscles, forget the tongue, the lips, the jaw. Hold fast to the visualization of the air space for each vowel as the air passes through it, accompanied by vibrations from the vocal folds. There are no complicated or gross movements required in changing into the positions for the vowel sounds. After these positions have been formed, there is no more movement in the mouth in order to continue making a vowel sound. The co-ordinated muscular activity from below continues its inward action against the lungs, to keep the current moving, while the vibrations from the vocal folds continue to affect the current of air, as it passes through the specific air space being held for its use, until the sounding time of the vowel is completed. In one sense the vowel is the connecting link between the consonants, in a syllable or a monosyllable. The vowel sound comes easily into its uses for speech, and serves to make continuity of sound, until the functioning for the following consonant is ready for use. The vowels also help in the projection of sound, thus making speech audible at greater distances.

The first essential in working on the vowels is to obtain continuity of sound, and the second is the effort toward the exact sound desired.

The main stimulations for the vowels are given by elevating or lowering the jaw, by stimulating the movements of the tongue, or by moving the lips, so that the air space within the mouth may be of definite shape and proportions.

The trainer helps the subject to prepare the oral cavity, and then gives the auditory pattern. The hearing child is given the auditory pattern simultaneously with the kinesthetic. The hard-of-hearing or the deaf are helped by feeling the vibrations, while sensing the pattern of movement through the kinesthetic and the tactile senses.

Not all of the vowels are listed in this chapter. Those are listed which are most commonly used in English words as follows:

The Front Vowels

	Webster Diacritical Markings	International Phonetic Alphabet*
e as in eat	ē	(i)
i as in it	ĭ	(I)
e as in egg	ĕ	(ε)
a as in at	ā	(æ)

A Central Vowel

u as in up	ŭ	(ʌ)

The Back Vowels

o as in top	ŏ	(ɒ)
a as in all (or *aw* as in jaw)	ạ	(ɔ)
a as in arm	ä	(a)
oo as in foot	o͝o	(U)
oo as in food	o͞o	(u)

---

* G. W. Gray and C. M. Wise, *op. cit.*

THE DIPHTHONGS

a as in ate	ā	(eI)
i as in ice	ī	(aI)
o as in oat	ō	(oU)
u as in use	ū	(ju)
ou as in out (or	ou	(aU)
ow as in cow)		
oi as in oil (or		
oy as in boy)	oi	(ɔI)

The stimulations will now be given for the production of the individual vowel sounds and also for the production of sequences in which
the vowel is used with the voiceless consonants, already described in Chapter Three. In fusing the stimulations for the single sounds into sequence,
the objective is to lead the mouth through the normal vocalization of the
sequence of sounds, with no pause between sounds.

Stimulations for the Front Vowels

STIMULATION FOR THE SOUND OF *e* AS IN "EAT"

The lower jaw is lowered slightly from a closed position, bringing
the lips apart and toward the corners, more than for any other vowel
sound. The incisors usually show. Because the jaws are nearly closed,
the surface of the tongue is very close to the dental ridge. Place thumb
and forefinger over the dental ridge outside, somewhat removed from
the mid-line, above the upper lip. Press at these two points. The pressure
should be exerted over the two areas to which the sides of the tongue are
expected to rise—a stimulation which tends to bring the sides of the
tongue upward to the dental ridge, in response to the outside pressure.
The central line of the tongue is left unstimulated. A groove is needed
there, larger than that required for the *s* sound. Give the auditory stimulation. The air, with accompanying vibrations, moves down through the
groove and out at the mid-line, between the two rows of incisors. At
times it is helpful to press along the central line of the tongue with a piece
of a tongue depressor, wider than the stimulation which might be given
by using the edge of the depressor.

Combinations are given first for practice of two-sound sequences. To
stimulate *fe*, follow the directions for the stimulation of *f* as given in
Chapter Three. The teacher's thumb and forefinger are below the lower
lip at the close of the *f* stimulation. Without lifting them, move the lower
lip and jaw slightly away from the upper teeth, then move toward the
corners, ready for the long *e* sound. Before the sound of *f* ceases, the *e*
sound should be begun, bringing *fe*, instead of *f--e*. Were we to reverse
the order, and stimulate *ef*, the *e* would be stimulated first, and without

lifting the hand from the lower jaw, bring the lower lip up quickly to the edge of the upper incisors, while the *e* is still sounding. In stimulating *te*, follow the directions in Chapter Three for the *t* sound. As soon as the escape of air is heard for the *t* sound, move the lips to the corners for *e*, while raising the jaw slightly. In reversing the order for *et*, stimulate the *e* sound first. As soon as it is heard, and while still sounding, make the stimulation for the *t* sound.

The student-teacher will need practice to move her fingers deftly enough to permit the second stimulation to come in correct timing. This skill comes only through practice.

Student practice for the sound of e *as in "eat" for two-sound sequences*:

fe	ke	et	es
pe	he	ep	ech
te	se	ek	esh

Perhaps a description of two or three of the stimulations for the three-sound sequences will be sufficient to enable the student to work out the rest. Stimulate the first two sounds as if spoken, without a break in sound, then add the third sound immediately. The infant babbles in this way first, "ba, ba," etc. Later he adds the final sounds. In the same way, when directing syllables or words composed of three sounds, and starting with a consonant, teach the vowel as belonging with the preceding consonant. Note that this close union is always brought about by moving immediately into the vowel position, *as soon as the first consonant sound is heard*, thus keeping the continuation of sound without a break. If the consonant is a continuant, the consonant sound will be heard as the position for the vowel is stimulated. If the preceding consonant is a plosive, the vowel position should be ready for sounding as soon as the puff of air is made, without break in sound.

Stimulation for "feet."—Stimulate *fe* as just described. While the *e* is still sounding, the teacher removes her fingers from the *e* position and stimulates the *t* sound. If there is a slight break in sound between the *fe* and the oncoming *t*, when first practiced, it is not likely to lead to a permanently incorrect habit. More practice will lead to the immediate addition of the *t* sound. Any pattern set which would separate the first consonant sound from the following vowel sets a pattern which would tend to confuse the learning process. "Fee-t"—and not "f-ee-t."

Stimulation for "sheet" (three sounds).—With thumb and forefinger of one hand at the corners of the mouth on the upper jaw and a similar position with the other hand on the lower jaw, bring the fingers and thumbs toward the mid-line, pressing on the *upper* jaw during the movement. (See stimulation for *sh* in Chapter Three.) The lips close the *sh* stimulation in a scoop-like shape, pressing slightly outward, and held firmly in this position, while the *sh* sound moves forth. When timing for the *sh* sound is concluded, the teacher quickly reverses the lip movements, and draws them back to the corners for the *e* to be made. Thus "she" is made in direct continuity. The stimulation for the *t* sound is quickly added, making the whole word in continuity. Practice in the same way will bring about the normally spoken word.

Student practice for three-sound sequences containing e *as in "eat," combined with voiceless consonants:*

heat	seat	wheat
feet	sheet	teach
pete	cheat	heath

STIMULATION FOR THE SOUND OF *i* AS IN "IT"

The stimulation for *i* as in "it" is used to bring a dip at the mid-line, along the end of the tongue. Lower the jaw a little more than for *e* in "eat." Draw the lips slightly toward the corners as if making room for the sound to come out clearly. An outside stimulation is that of pressing along the mid-line of the lower lip with the narrow edge of a tongue depressor, about halfway down on the outside of the jaw. This outside pressure tends to stimulate the dip to the mid-line of the tongue inside. Give the auditory stimulation. Repeat two or three times. An inside stimulation is to dip the mid-line of the end of the tongue with the edge of the tongue depressor, at different intervals, until the form comes more easily. Then try the outside stimulation again, as sequences are practiced.

Stimulations for "if."—Move the lips slightly to the corners with one hand. Stimulate the mid-line dip of the tongue end with the other hand. Give the auditory pattern. As soon as the *i* (as in "it") is heard, move the lower lip to the edge of the upper teeth for the *f* sound.

Student practice for the sound of i *as in "it," combined with voiceless consonants:*

if	ik	ith	si	chi
it	ish	fi	hi	thi
ip	iss	pi	shi	ki

Stimulations for "pick" (three-sound sequence).—Move the lower lip and jaw upward to contact the upper lip. (See directions for *p* in Chapter Three.) As the reversal of movement occurs, the escape of air for the *p* is heard, but the teacher continues straight downward into the position for *i* as in "it." As soon as the *i* is heard, and while still sounding, the teacher stimulates the *k* sound.

Student practice for the three-sound sequences containing i *as in "it," combined with voiceless consonants:*

hitch	fit	pick	tit
which	kit	pitch	chit
whit	pith	pip	fish

STIMULATION FOR THE SOUND OF *e* AS IN "EGG"

Lower the jaw, slightly more than that for *i* in "it." Move lips slightly toward the corners. This vowel sound is stimulated by directing the air current, accompanied by the vibrations, to the tip of the tongue. The outside stimulation is a pressure at one point only, at the mid-line, just below the lower lip. The index finger seems best adapted for this stimulation, or the thin tip of the tongue depressor, but at one point only. Sound *e* as in "egg." Do not expect that the muscles will adapt themselves fully the first time the stimulation is applied. Repeat the stimulation, then drop it for another application of the same stimulation at a later time. The shape of the tongue at the tip for *e* as in "egg" is narrowed toward the mid-line. The effect may be obtained, in cases where the outward stimulation fails to work, by pressing the two sides of the end of the tongue toward the mid-line, with the two halves of the tongue depressor, while at the same time dipping the tongue end behind the lower incisors. The subject feels this tongue end stimulation and tends to send the sound forward to that point. Even if the *e* sound as in "egg" is not entirely satisfactory at first, continue the stimulation for the following sound immediately. Repetition at repeated intervals brings better results in time.

Stimulations for "ef" (e as in "egg").—Place the tip of the forefinger at the mid-point directly below the lower lip. Bring the jaw downward, by means of the pressure of the forefinger, slightly lower than for *i* in "it." As soon as the vowel sound emerges, and while still sounding, quickly change the use of the forefinger to that of thumb and second finger on the lower jaw to bring the lower lip upward against the upper teeth for the *f* sound.

Student practice for the sound of e *as in "egg," combined with voiceless consonants:*

ef	esh	et	pe	she
eth	ech	ek	fe	che
es	ep	ke	se	te

PRACTICE OF THREE-SOUND STIMULATIONS FOR *e* AS IN "EGG"

Stimulations for "pet."—Place thumb and second finger on the lower jaw to control the movements for the *p* sound, reserving the forefinger for the vowel to follow. As soon as the puff of air is made, lift the thumb and second finger and press at the mid-point just below the lower lip for the short *e* sound. As soon as the vowel sound starts, remove the forefinger from the lower jaw, and with it make the stimulation for the *t* sound.

Further practice for e *as in "egg," combined with voiceless consonants:*

pet	het	chet
peck	hep	fetch
chess	whet	seth

STIMULATION FOR THE SOUND OF *a* AS IN "HAT"

Try the outside stimulation first. Place thumb and forefinger at equal distances from the mid-line, below the lower lip. With medium pressure, bring the lower jaw downward a little lower than for *e* in "egg." Next, the thumb and finger separate, pressing against the jaw as they move outward from the mid-line in an upward curve about halfway from the mid-line to the corners of the mouth. What we are seeking is to have the tongue end move downward behind the lower incisors, and broaden out. The movement over the lower jaw on the outside tends to bring the tongue behind the lower incisors. The teacher gives the auditory stimulation as she keeps her hold on the jaw in the last position. Another help is to place the tongue depressor flat on the surface of the front of the tongue, depressing the end behind the lower front teeth. The tongue depressor should rest on the edge of the lower teeth at about three-quarters of an inch from the end. The part of the depressor which is inside the mouth presses lightly against the surface of the tongue, shaping it like an inclined plane, sloping toward the tip. Sound *a* as in "at." The sound of *a* as in "care" is stimulated at the start as *a* in "at," followed by an upward movement of the tongue tip (which will be described under the stimulation for *r*, in Chapter Five). The student will follow the same general plan for stimulating the two sound-sequences, containing *a* as in "at," as in the previously directed front vowel combinations. Follow the specific directions for the *a* as in "at," wherever it occurs.

Student practice for the sound of a *as in "at," combined with voiceless consonants:*

at	ak	pa	sa
af	ash	ta	cha
ap	ach	ka	sha

Directions for three-sound stimulations containing a *as in "at."*—The first consonant, with the vowel following, is stimulated as a two-sound stimulation like those previously given. The last consonant is stimulated immediately afterward. The important thing for the student is to find through his practice the way by which the worker's stimulation may bring a normally spoken word.

Directions will now be given for the stimulation of a few three-sound words. These directions will serve as a pattern by which to work out others.

Practice for the stimulation of "fat."—Use first the stimulation for *f* as given in Chapter Three. When the sound is heard in the timing for normal speech, move the lower lip and jaw downward while the *f* sound is still sounding, into the *a* position as in "at." The teacher sounds *fa* in exact timing with the stimulations, not *f--a*, separating the two sounds. After *fa* is completed in normal timing, the stimulation for *t* is added.

Practice for the stimulation of "sack."—Keep in mind the stimulation for *s* as given in Chapter Three. Move the lower jaw into a position close to the upper one. The lips are drawn slightly to the corners. The air is being moved down the small central line depression for *s*. The teacher makes the hissing sound, while the mouth is being held briefly in this position. As she hears the *s* sound, even if not satisfactory at first, she moves the jaw quickly downward, into the *a* position (as in "at"), thus sounding *sa*, as in continuous speech. With the other hand, she immediately gives the stimulation for the *k* sound. (The *ck* is sounded as *k*.)

Further practice for the sound of a *as in* "at":

hat	pack	sack	thatch (3 sounds)
fat	whack	pat	tat
cat	sat	tap	chat

A Central Vowel

STIMULATION FOR THE SOUND OF *u* AS IN "UP"

Although the sound of *u* as in "up" is classified as a central vowel, the student may look to certain outside stimulations to help produce the sound. Let us start by recalling the stimulation of the *h* sound, as given in Chapter Three. The jaw is lowered and the upper pathway is opened, letting the whole air current flow through unimpeded. The picture is the same in many respects as for *u* in "up." The jaw is lowered and the upper pathway is opened up, but there the likeness ends. The kind of sound, i.e., the use of the air current, is different. The vibrations enter the picture for short *u*, and the current of air is moved *steadily* through the passageways, instead of being forced quickly and suddenly as for *h*.

This is the stimulation which may be used: the teacher lowers the jaw a little more than for *a* as in "at," and does not stimulate further muscular activity. She lowers it by a hold on the lowest part of the jaw, keeping the mouth open, while she makes the sound herself. The first sound in "above" and "about" is the same sound, and may be stimulated in the same way. The use of *a* as an article should also be taught as this same neutral sound, "a book" and "a girl," not *a* as in "ate." An easier flow of sounds is enhanced by this use of the sound for the article. This vowel comes in easily, between the processes which are necessary for the consonants. In the following practice, move immediately into the consonant stimulation, as soon as the short *u* is heard.

Student practice for the sound of u *as in* "up," *combined with voiceless consonants:*

uf	ut	ush	tu	shu
uth	uk	uch	ku	chu
up	us	thu	fu	hu

Further practice for the sound of u *as in* "up":

hut	cut	suck
shut	such	chuck
tut	sup	shuck

Back Vowels

STIMULATION FOR THE SOUND OF *o* AS IN "TOP"

Put thumb and forefinger at points halfway between the mid-line and the corners of the mouth below the lower lip. Pressing inward, move the jaw straight downward, slightly lower than for *u* as in "up." With the other hand, move the upper lip outward slightly and a little to the center. Give the auditory stimulation.

Student practice for the sound of o *as in "top," combined with voiceless consonants:*

ot	op	ho	po	sho
off	ok	fo	to	cho
os	osh	tho	ko	so

Further practice for the sound of o *as in "top."*—Stimulate the first two sounds as a blended whole. Add the final consonant.

hot	shop	top	hock
hop	chop	cop	sock
fop	pop	shock	tock

STIMULATION FOR THE SOUND OF *a* AS IN "ALL" OR "CAW"

With one hand move the jaw downward, not quite as far as for *o* in "top." Let the hand in contact with the lower jaw press the lips slightly toward the middle and outward. Place the thumb and forefinger of the other hand lightly on the surface of the throat in a position similar to that for stimulating the *k* sound. Draw the digits forward lightly, slanting downward as they approach the front. This stimulation tends to enlarge the oropharyngeal cavity.

Since the stimulations for the voiceless consonants only have been described up to this point, the student may first practice the following list, and add to the practice after taking up the voiced consonants, especially the *l* as in "ball."

caw	paw	aught	chalk
haw	faucet	saw	talk
thaw	caught	shaw	chaw

STIMULATION FOR THE SOUND OF *a* AS IN "ARM"

Move the lower jaw downward, very slightly lower than for *a* in "at." The lips are drawn back from the mid-line against the jaws, showing incisors. Give the auditory stimulation. If the sound is not forthcoming, the tongue is not dipping sufficiently along the mid-line. A tongue depressor may be inserted and made to press firmly downward by using the narrow edge along the mid-line from the front to the back. The sensing of this stimulation is effective, but the process is not pleasant, so do not use it until other means have failed. A visual stimulation, in which a paper tongue or a plasticine tongue is treated in a similar manner by the tongue depressor, is sometimes sufficient stimulation without using the inside method.

Student practice for the sound of a *as in "arm."*—Until voiced consonants are taken up, the practice on this sound is somewhat limited. (See Chapter Five.)

ha	ca
pa	sa
fa	ta

STIMULATION FOR THE SOUND OF *OO* AS IN "FOOT"

Look into the mirror at your own mouth as you make this sound. The shaping of the exterior to conform to the normal appearance is an important factor in producing it. Note the shape of the opening formed, through which the vibrating air is to move.

The teacher may place the thumb and forefinger of one hand on the upper jaw toward the corners of the lips, and thumb and forefinger of the other hand on the lower jaw in a similar position. She moves toward the mid-line with both hands simultaneously, and brings the lips outward in a scoop-like position. The work of the hand on the upper jaw is merely to move the lips and adjacent parts into this outward position. No pressure is needed against the upper jaw. The hand on the lower jaw exerts pressure to be brought against the lower jaw, and at the same time moves to shape the lower lip. This lower pressure tends to bring about a lowering of the back of the tongue, preparatory to making the sound in question as the lips are held in the position noted.

Student practice for the sound of oo *as in "foot," combined with voiceless consonants:*

foot	took	shook
hook	cook	soot

STIMULATION FOR THE SOUND OF *OO* AS IN "FOOD"

Here again it helps to see the outward, visible moving of your mouth in the mirror as *oo* in "food" is made. Note the size and shape of the opening formed. The picture is that of the air current, accompanied by vibrations, being pressed in an even, steady stream from below, first through the larger space inside the mouth, then outward through a narrowed-down opening at the lips, as it leaves the passageways. As in all of the moto-kinesthetic stimulations, the teacher works to aid the muscles to find the way to achieve a standard goal. In this case, she moves the lips from the corners toward the mid-line, making a small opening for the passage of the vibrating air. Note the fine lines along the lips as they move closer to the mid-line through this stimulation. At this point the auditory stimulation, with hearing children, is generally enough to produce the sound.

Student practice for the sound of oo *as in "food," combined with the voiceless consonants:*

food	coop	coot	shoot
hoot	toot	stoop	choo

The Diphthongs

STIMULATION FOR THE SOUND OF *a* AS IN "ATE"

In stimulating the diphthongs, the teacher's auditory pattern continues sound without a break between the two parts of the diphthong. To start the first sound of the diphthong *a* as in "ate," place thumb and forefinger on the lower jaw about halfway from the mid-line to the corners. Press against the jaw and bring it downward at the same time, not quite as low as for *a* in "at." The pressure is a stimulation to the sides of the tongue to move downward. Start to sound the *a* as in "ate," and then immediately move the lower jaw upward until the position for *i* as in "it" is reached. Move thumb and forefinger slightly toward the corners, without lifting them, as *i* in "it" is stimulated.

It is not possible to pause after the first sound of the diphthong to dip the tongue end for the closing sound, as is suggested when first stimulating the vowel *i* as in "it." Bring the lower jaw to the short *i* position and hold the lips slightly toward the corners of the mouth to close the diphthong. The final stimulation should end very close to that of the long *e* as in "me."

Student practice for the diphthong a *as in "ate," combined with voiceless consonants:*

ate	fake	cake	pate
hate	they	fate	pace
take	chase	sate	shape
sake	Kate	chafe	shake

STIMULATION FOR THE SOUND OF *i* AS IN "ICE"

The first sound of this diphthong is the same as the *a* in "arm." Therefore lower the jaw, start the auditory pattern, and then move directly upward into the position of the jaw for *i* in "it," and at the same time moving the lips toward the corners. Do not stop to dip the tongue for the closing sound *i* as in "it." If necessary practice the short *i* position separately, associating position with sound. Continue sounding throughout the processes. There is no break in sound as the first sound merges into the second.

Student practice for the sound of i *as in "ice," combined with voiceless consonants:*

fight	kite	thigh
hike	site	shy
pike	hie	sigh
eye	tight	tike

STIMULATION FOR THE SOUND OF *o* AS IN "OAT"

Move the jaw downward with thumb and forefinger, not quite so far as for *o* in "not." When the lowest point is reached, begin pressing by degrees toward the mid-line, bringing the jaw upward again. The teacher's other hand works on the upper jaw, moving the part above the upper lip into a rounding position, as soon as the lower jaw begins to move upward. A larger rounding movement comes first which is more than lip movement, and lastly, both lips move into the final position, which is like *oo* in "foot." There is no break in sound between the two parts.

Student practice for the sound of o *as in "oat," combined with voiceless consonants:*

hope	coat	show
pope	soap	choke
cope	poke	coke

STIMULATION FOR THE SOUND OF *u* AS IN "USE"

The first part of the stimulation for this diphthong is the same as that for *e* in "eat." After the *e* position has been stimulated, the thumb and finger at the corners above the upper lip begin to move toward the center, pressing firmly against the upper jaw as they move, tending to bring the sound of the consonant *y*. (See Chapter Five for *y*.) Continue movement toward the center, without lifting the fingers, until the sound of *oo* as in "food" is stimulated. This sound of *u* is made up of the sequence *e--yoo*. The long *e* sound is stopped quickly.

Student practice of the sound of u *as in "use," combined with voiceless consonants.*—If a consonant precedes the long *u* sound, stimulate the consonant and move immediately into the *e* sound as in "eat," then finish as previously indicated. The sound of *u* as in "use" is also represented by *ew*.

uf	ute	uk	tu	cute
uth	fu	hu	ku	stew
uk	use	few	tew	chute

STIMULATION FOR THE SOUND OF *ou* AS IN "OUT"

Bring the lower jaw downward as for *a* in "arm." Make the sound as an auditory pattern. Then, with both hands, move the parts above and below the lips outward and toward the center, first making a larger outlet, then decreasing the size of the outlet as the movement continues, until the position for *oo* as in "foot" is reached.

Student practice for the sound of ou *as in "out," with voiceless consonants only:*

how	couch	chow
out	south	cow
ouch	pouch	pow

STIMULATION FOR THE SOUND OF *oi* AS IN "OIL" OR *oy* IN "TOY"

Start the mouth as for *a* in "all." This has brought the lips and sur-rounding parts outward and tending toward the mid-line. As soon as the *a* in "all" is heard, move the lips away from the mid-line, directly into the position for *i* as in "it."

Student practice for the sound of oi *as in "oil" or* oy *as in "toy"* (practice is limited, until voiced consonants are studied) :

foy	toy	hoist
oys	coy	choice
poy	soy	foist

CHAPTER FIVE

THE VOICED CONSONANTS

We started our study of the consonant sounds with those that use the air current without the vibrations of the vocal cords. They are the voiceless consonants. Next, we considered the sounds which come with a steady, even flow of the current after definite positions have been obtained, and which make use of the vibrations of the vocal cords to produce sounds through resonance. These are the vowels. Now we come to the consonant sounds which require not only a definite muscular activity, but which also make use of the vibrations as a part of their production. These are the voiced consonants. They are represented by the following symbols:

VOICED CONSONANTS

Webster's Dictionary	International Phonetic Alphabet*	Webster's Dictionary	International Phonetic Alphabet*
v	v	j	dʒ
th	ð	m	m
b	b	n	n
d	d	ng	ŋ
g	g	l	l
z	z	r	r
zh	ʒ	w	w
		y	j

* G. W. Gray and C. M. Wise, *op. cit.*

STIMULATION FOR THE SOUND OF *v*

To produce the sound of *v*, the teacher starts the stimulation in the same way as for *f*, but brings the lower lip into firmer contact with the edges of the upper teeth. While this firm contact is being held, the vibrating air is forced upward. The auditory stimulation along with the firm pressure in the correct position tends to produce the sound in question with the hearing child, while the child with hearing difficulty gets his stimulation not only through the feel of the correct position but by the feeling of the vibrations as his hand contacts his teacher while speaking. As soon as the *v* sound is heard in normal timing, and while it is sounding, move the mouth directly into the vowel position.

Student practice for the sound of v:

vac	vex	save
vat	vox	stove
vast	have	stave

STIMULATION FOR THE VOICED *th* SOUND
(Read Again Chapter Three, for Voiceless *th*)

Stimulate the tongue to contact the edge of the upper incisors the same as for the voiceless *th*. If the tongue depressor is used, press it along the edge of the upper teeth to give the subject the feeling of this curved edge toward which the tongue is to move. Hold the tongue more firmly against the teeth than is done for the voiceless *th*, to help bring the vibrations through.

Another stimulation which may help the tongue to come to the curved edge of the upper teeth is for the teacher to curve an index finger over the upper lip. With it bring the upper lip down as close as possible to the edge of the upper teeth, pressing inward. The tongue feels this pressure, and tends to come toward it. The teacher makes the voiced sound of *th*. As soon as the *th* sound is heard, and while it is still sounding, move the mouth into the position for the vowel to follow. (The student is limited in the words to be practiced until he completes the voiced consonants.)

Student practice for the sound of voiced th:

that	seethe
this	though
thus	thou

PRODUCTION OF THE SOUNDS OF *b, d, g*

Conditions which affect all three in the same way.—These sounds are made by first stimulating a firm closure. The vocal folds vibrate simultaneously with the completion of this activity of muscles. Force from below builds up the air pressure behind the part closing off the current. The sound is begun in an enclosed area. Suddenly, the part of the mouth which has closed off the current is opened, permitting the air to escape, as the mouth moves immediately into the position for the vowel to follow. The conditions for the functioning of the air are the same in all three sounds, but the current is stopped and acted upon in three different locations.

Since the three air chambers into which the vibrating air is pressed are of different size and shape, there is a variation in sound effect as the functioning for *b, d,* and *g* occurs.

STIMULATION FOR THE SOUND OF *b*

For *b*, the teacher places the forefinger and thumb of one hand above the upper lip, and those of the other hand below the lower lip, to bring the lips together with pressure. Muscles in both the upper and the lower lip are stimulated to move firmly together, then to separate immediately in order to move into the next sound process.

Let us begin practice with the *b* sound followed by *a* as in "at." The finger and thumb of the teacher's hand which is in contact with the lower jaw may be placed as for *a* in "at." (See Chapter Three.) In this position on the lower jaw, move the lower lip upward, to contact the upper lip as the teacher brings it downward with the other hand at the same time.

Visualize, in a slowed-down picture, the compression of the air behind the closed lips, while vibrations pass into this closed area. Picture the equal forces from above and below which press the two lips together, and hold them firmly momentarily to keep the compressed air inside. Now picture the same process as taking place in normal timing. The two lips are held against each other with equal force, then are simultaneously pulled apart. The hand in contact with the lower lip draws it downward and directly into position for *a* as in "at."

Student practice for the sound of b:

baf	back	cub
bath	bas	bab
bat	bash	bap

In stimulating *bab* or *cub*, do not move the lower lip downward on the final *b*. Let the lips part without further sound, after the beginning of the final *b* is heard. Otherwise a vowel sound will follow the final *b* sound.

There is a fine differentiation between the stimulations for *p* and for *b*, but a careful carrying out of these differences in stimulation may make the difference between correct and incorrect habits later on, as these sounds appear in speech. When *p* is stimulated, the teacher does not touch the upper lip. The lower lip is trained to move against the upper lip with firmness, and quickly down again, while with *b* the lips are pressed against each other with equal force but are held together in normal timing only, to be quickly separated and moved into the vowel to follow.

Further practice for the sound of b:

cab	bit	hob	bait
stab	bib	bought	beat
beth	fib	bus	beach
best	fob	but	beak

PRODUCTION OF THE SOUND OF *d*

The place for closing off the air current is at the dental ridge. The part which moves to close it off is the front of the tongue, as the tip presses forward toward the mid-point of the dental ridge. The edges of the blade contact the dental ridge at the sides to hold back the air. The contact is a firm one. The area back of the tongue is enclosed, as the vibrations pass into it. There is pressure from below as if to force the air toward the front, above the tongue, but there is also pressure of the muscles of the tongue, as if in an effort to prevent the escape of this compressed air until the vibrations have done their part and the time has come to release the air. The lips are slightly drawn to the corners.

STIMULATION FOR THE SOUND OF *d*

The description above gives us some clues as to the required stimulations. To bring the tongue tip forward, and at the same time to stimulate pressure inside, against the dental ridge, press on the outside at the mid-line above the upper lip, to indicate the point inside to which the tip of the tongue is to come. The pressure is much firmer than in the stimulation for *t*. The teacher keeps in mind that the sound of *d* is begun while the tongue maintains its firm position against the dental ridge. Move lips slightly toward the corners. The mouth should not be opened wide for this tongue-end stimulation. A slight separation between the two rows of incisors, as in normal speech, sets a more correct pattern for the total process. The teacher should not make an exaggerated pattern herself, intending it as a visual aid to the subject. The help for these sounds comes better through the feeling of the stimulation than through the visual pattern. The teacher should visualize the process for each sound. The sound of *t* brings the picture of the air current as released by means of the quick action of the tongue end downward. The sound of *d* is begun inside the closed area, and is completed as the tongue end ceases its closure, and is moved into the position for the following vowel sound.

In cases where the subject needs more help to raise the tongue end to the dental ridge, the teacher may insert a tongue depressor under the end of the tongue, bringing it by a very direct quick move, straight upward against the dental ridge. The incisors should not be any farther apart than is necessary to get the depressor inside and under the tongue. The teacher's movement must be quick and decisive so that the tongue end may have no time to move away. If she succeeds in pinning the tongue against the dental ridge, she makes the auditory stimulation, slips the depressor out quickly, and moves into the vowel to follow.

When the teacher's stimulation for the final *d* is given, care must be observed that the tongue remains in the *d* position to end the word, and that no vowel sound follows. Simply press at the mid-line point, and let that end the stimulation for the final *d*. If a sequence like "Dad and I" were being stimulated, the jaw would be lowered for *a* (in "and") after "dad" is completed. In the beginning of practice for the *d* sound, the suggestion is to practice with the same vowel following, until the two sounds move out as in normal speech. Let us begin with *a* as in "at."

Student practice for the sound of d, *followed by* a *as in "at"* :

daf	dat	das	had	thad
dath	dak	dad	fad	cad
dap	dash	dab	sad	pad

Further practice for the sound of d, *used with other vowels:*

deck	dick	hod	bud	do
fed	dif	shod	thud	paid
ted	dith	pod	dud	dote
sed	sid	cod	sud	dude

STIMULATION OF THE SOUND OF *g*

The third in this series of sounds in which the air current is closed off, as for *b* and *d*, is the sound of *g* as in "go." This time the back of the tongue rises to the soft palate to effect the closure. The area below this closure is the airtight space into which the vibrations pass during the time in which this condition is held. The air is pressed upward from below by the air controls against the temporary wall which has risen to impede its progress. Since the beginning of the sound is made while the air space is enclosed, differing from the sound of *c*, the compressed air would tend to force its way outward. Therefore the back of the tongue must hold with firmness until the sound effect sought is begun sufficiently to be heard. Then, the beginning sound having been achieved, the back of the tongue moves downward, and the vowel follows immediately.

To stimulate this procedure, the teacher places thumb and forefinger on the outside, in the same position as for the stimulation of *c*. The teacher presses upward and inward, giving the feeling to the parts to stay closed. The sound of *g* is begun while the temporary wall (the back of the tongue) is being held inside. Simultaneously with this closure, the vibrations begin their work. The auditory stimulation is given at this point with hearing subjects, and the feeling of the teacher's vibrations for the hard-of-hearing. The teacher does not stimulate any downward movement of the back of the tongue for the end of the *g* stimulation as for the *c*, since resonance in the part below the closure produces the beginning of the sound required, which then is completed as it blends with the vowel following. The immediate stimulation of the vowel sound, as soon as the voiced *g* is heard, makes the two sounds spoken as in normal speech. When the sloweddown process is clearly visualized, picture the same process in quicker tempo, as in normal speech.

If more help is needed to get muscular action started correctly, insert a tongue depressor to extend over the surface of the tongue, about one-third of the way back. In this position, press toward the back, pushing the back upward. To place the depressor farther back may cause discomfort. When the closure is made, the auditory stimulation is given, or else the feeling of vibrations. The tongue may be drawn into the vowel shape for *a* as in "at" without lifting the tongue depressor. Let us begin the practice with the stimulation for the *g* sound followed by that of *a* as in "at."

Student practice for the sound of g:

gab	gap	shag	fag
gad	gas	sag	hag
gash	bag	tag	gag

Further practice for the sound of g, *followed by other vowels:*

gay	guide	bug	dug
gate	go	thug	gust
gape	goat	pug	gut
geese	dig	chug	good

When the *g* sound ends the word, the teacher's fingers press upward and inward, but cease all stimulations there, leaving the back of the tongue to relax unstimulated, as the next sound comes on. Otherwise a vowel sound may follow the *g* sound, *bug-u* (*u* as in *up*).

STIMULATION FOR THE SOUND OF *z*

(See Again Voiceless *s* in Chapter Three)

The stimulations for the position of the mouth to make the *z* sound are the same as for the voiceless *s*. The vibrations from the vocal folds, however, are added in the production of the *z* sound. The teacher presses more firmly with thumb and forefinger outside the upper jaw than for the *s* sound. This tends to bring the vibrations through, as the teacher makes the sound, or the hard-of-hearing feel the vibrations.

Student practice for the voiced s *or* z *sound:*

as	fiz	buzz	chews
has	puz	sez	dues
fez	does	boos	is

STIMULATION FOR THE SOUND OF *zh*

Follow the same procedure as for *sh*, except that the outside stimulation on the upper jaw is more firm than for the *sh* sound. The firmer stimulation tends to bring the vibrations through.

Student practice for the zh *sound:*

azure	mirage
garage	beige

STIMULATION FOR THE SOUND OF *j*

In stimulating the *j* sound, the fore part of the blade of the tongue is raised by outward stimulation as in forming *ch*. The vocal folds vibrate, and there is no necessity for quick release as in *ch*. The teacher moves the lower jaw into a closed position—in which molars approximate each other, the upper jaw being stimulated by outward pressure, the lips being moved toward the center and outward in a scoop-like appearance—as for *sh, zh, ch,* and *j*. One difference lies in the fact that *sh* and *ch* are voiceless, while *zh* and *j* are voiced. *Sh* and *ch* differ also in that the trainer moves a steady stream of air outward for *sh*. *Ch* requires the quick immediate expulsion of air. The trainer's pressure on the upper jaw is less for *zh* than for *j*, both of which are voiced. As in the case for stimulating other sequences, while the *j* is sounding, move the jaw downward or into the vowel to follow.

Student practice for the sound of j :

jack	jip	stage	jo
jap	page	cage	joke
jest	sage	jake	jute

PRODUCTION OF THE SOUNDS OF *m, n, ng*

Conditions which affect all three in the same way.—As in the other two groups of three sounds previously described, the air current is closed again in the three possible locations for such closures—at the lips, at the dental ridge, and at the back of the tongue. The closure is made first. Simultaneously with this accomplishment, the vocal folds vibrate, but this time the vibrating air is sent upward through the nasal passages and out through the nostrils. To induce nasality, pressure on the bridge of the nose is advised, rather than at the end of the nose, or at one side. The finger pressed on the bone at the mid-line gives a stable pressure, and a stimulation, which is at the mid-line between the two nostrils, through which the vibrating air is to pass. However, if the teacher wishes the subject to feel her vibrations, as she makes these sounds, he may feel them more definitely by touching one of the sides of her nose rather than at the bridge. These sounds require a steady, even action on the part of the muscles which control the air, and there is an economical use of the air current when functioning.

STIMULATION FOR THE SOUND OF *m*

With thumb and forefinger placed on the lower jaw, below the lower lip, equidistant from the mid-line, move the jaw with the lower lip upward until it contacts the upper lip. Do not touch the upper lip; at least, not under usual conditions. Do not press the lower lip against the upper. All that is required in this case is an easy contact of the lips for *m*. In this use for *m*, the air is not compressed back of the closure. It is not pressing to come out through the mouth, as it has a way out through the nasal passages; therefore the lips are not required to hold firmly together in order to withstand air pressure as for *b*.

Place a finger of the other hand firmly on the bridge of the nose, while the teacher is holding the lower lip in contact with the upper one. Give the auditory stimulation for the hearing child, and let the hard-of-hearing feel the vibrations. As soon as the sound of *m* is made, move the jaw immediately into the position required by the vowel which follows.

Let us again start our practice, with the *a* as in "at" following the *m*. As the teacher moves the lip and jaw downward, her hands are in position to stimulate this vowel, without moving them from the first position for *m*. When *m* follows a vowel, move the lower lip upward immediately to contact the upper one (as soon as the vowel sound is heard sufficiently). It is not necessary to stop to release the vowel position. In stimulating "home," for instance, the mouth is in the rounded position for *o* when the *m* process comes into the sequence. Remove the hand from the upper jaw, which has been rounding the upper lip. Without lifting the hand below, move the lower lip upward against the upper to finish the word with *m*. You will note that the rounded position yields immediately as the *m* is stimulated. When *m* is the final sound, stimulate it as given above, but do not move the lower lip downward until the *m* sound ceases, or a vowel sound will be heard.

Student practice for the sound of m, *followed by* a *as in "at," and other vowels:*

map	met	mut	mote	muse
mat	med	mate	mode	come
mash	mesh	made	mope	home
match	mit	mete	mute	shame

STIMULATION FOR THE SOUND OF *n*

Starting with a closed position of the mouth, the teacher moves the lower jaw and lip downward slightly, separating the lips. The hand on the lower jaw may move the lips a little toward the corners. A finger of the other hand is pressed firmly on the bridge of the nose, high enough to feel the solid bony structure of the upper part at the mid-line. Keep the hold on the lower lip, so that it cannot move upward to contact the upper lip as is done for the *m* sound. A common error is to substitute one of these sounds for the other. Be sure that outwardly lips are together for *m* but separated for the *n* sound. Hold them for *n* in that position. It helps also for the child to feel his front teeth between the parted lips with one of his fingers, to strengthen the feeling of separation of the lips for the *n* sound. With the mouth in this position give the auditory stimulation. The sound of *n* may come without further effort. The stimulation on the bridge of the nose, at a point higher up than the tongue end, tends to bring the tongue end upward inside, since the tongue tends to move toward a point of pressure. It aids sometimes to press lightly at the midpoint above the upper lip, giving a steady, even pressure, while the lips are kept apart. The pressure should not be as strong as for the stimulation for *d*, nor should the stimulation be given, as for *t*, to move downward quickly, since a downward movement of the tongue is not a part of the stimulation for the *n* sound. The downward movement will come normally as the jaw moves into the vowel position. If the production of the *n* sound needs more help than has been suggested, the tongue depressor may be inserted, under the tongue, mouth opened only wide enough to allow the depressor to enter. Move the tongue depressor upward with a quick movement to enable it to hold the tip of the tongue against the dental ridge, before it can move otherwise. Again give the sound stimulation, and if the subject is able to respond, move the jaw downward into the vowel position to bring about the immediate sounding of the first two sounds. The aim is, after the beginning efforts, to have them spoken as in normal speech—not as two separate sounds.

In visualizing the use of the air current for *n*, the student will bear in mind that the tongue end does not need to press as firmly against the dental ridge as for *d*, because it does not need to withstand the pressure of compressed air, back and over it. It needs to be stimulated only firmly enough to hold its contact during the sounding, since the force of the air pressure in the mouth is minimized by having an outlet through the nasal passages. When stimulating the final *n*, give the stimulation and stop. Let the mouth relax naturally. Any further stimulation might result in an added vowel sound. To stimulate *na* as in "nat," follow the directions to stimulate the *n* sound. One of the teacher's hands is holding the lips apart, and somewhat to the corners. As soon as the *n* sound is begun, and while it is still being sounded, move the jaw downward, without lifting the hand from the jaw, into the shape for the *a* in "at."

Student practice for the sound of n:

nat	tan	net	pin	tone
nash	pan	neck	not	nut
nap	dan	ned	nob	nude
nab	can	knit	none	noon
nag	ban	nip	note	nine

STIMULATION FOR THE SOUND OF *ng*

As stated previously, the production of the sound represented by *ng* is similar to those represented by *m* and *n*. The location for stopping the air current for *ng* is at the back of the mouth. In normal speech the back of the tongue rises, prevents the air current from coming through the mouth, and sends the vibrating air through the nasal passages. If the student has followed the previous stimulations carefully, he will doubtless be able to work out the stimulations for the *ng* himself. First, lower the jaw. With thumb and forefinger on the outside below the base of the tongue, in the same location as for *k* and *g*, press gently upward, then hold this position with one hand, while pressing on the bridge of the nose with the other. As in the stimulations for *m* and *n*, there is no further activity of muscles in the mouth in order to make this sound, after the position has been assumed. The steady movement of the muscles which control the air and the vibrations of the vocal folds do the rest. With the sound of *ng*, there is no need of pressure by the back of the tongue against the soft palate above, more than to keep it in contact with the soft palate, since the air current is not held compressed for this sound as for *g*, but moves steadily outward through the nasal passages.

If more help is needed to get the tongue to assume the desired shape, a tongue depressor may be inserted, and used first to dip the end of the tongue. While holding the end down, without lifting the depressor, push the tongue gently back and up. Hold this position, while the pressure is being exerted on the bridge of the nose, to produce the nasal tone desired.

This sound, unlike *m* and *n*, occurs only at the close of syllables or monosyllables. In the practice of the stimulations, as soon as the vowel preceding *ng* is heard in normal timing, start the stimulation to close with *ng*. In the word "bang," for instance, stimulate *ba* as previously indicated in Chapter Three. Then stimulate the *ng*.

Student practice for the sound of ng :

hang	bang	thing	dong
fang	gang	king	gong
pang	tang	ong	sung
sang	sing	song	hung

In a few words, like England, "ing" is stimulated first, then "gland" afterward, which starts the last syllable with a hard *g* sound. "Longer" is another word similarly sounded. A common mistake, among people who have spoken certain languages other than English, is to sound the *ng* in "king" as the nasal *ng* first, then to add a *g* sound. The nasal only should end such words.

PRODUCTION OF THE SOUNDS OF *l* AND *r*

In the production of the sounds of *l* and *r*, there are two parts to be considered. First, the current is moved upward, as if to continue in a steady stream, by the muscles which control the air. The vocal folds bring vibrations into the picture. The air current is pressed through a very definite chamber or opening. This is the first part, the result of which is vocalization. Visualize the process as a slowed-down picture. After the current gets started and vocalization has begun, a sudden change comes which disrupts the current, through a quick movement of the jaw and tongue, forcing a readjustment of the molecules. (See Chapter One on uses of the air current.) The consonant part of the sound comes at the point of this sudden change, causing conflict and readjustment of the particles of air.

STIMULATION FOR THE SOUND OF *l*

In the case of the *l* sound, the resonance chamber through which the vibrating air first passes is formed back of the tongue blade, whose broadened tip contacts the dental ridge and keeps the air current from escaping at the front. Its way of escape is through the openings, one on each side, formed between the back sides of the tongue and the molars. Therefore, as we consider the conditions to be met, we are helped to determine the stimulations needed. If the air is to be pressed through definite openings at the sides of the tongue, the conclusion is that the current must be shut off elsewhere. The front part of the tongue acts in this capacity as it broadens out and holds against the dental ridge, to block all escape of air in front. The slowed-down picture now lets us see the sides of the tongue as fitting along closely to the dental ridge, upper gums, and inside of the molars, until it dips as it approaches the back molars leaving the openings. Our picture allows us to think of the whole current, as it is being pressed upward from below. It enters the mouth and is pressed into all available air space, but the two small side openings are its only way of escape. It must pass through these openings with the force of the total air current back of it, under pressure from below. The vibrations are at work. The movements to be stimulated are those which can help to bring about this particular use of the air current. The front part of the tongue must find the way to stop the air current. There is need of no more pressure of the tongue against the dental ridge than is necessary to hold it in position, during the short period used in the first part of the process.

The first step in the stimulation of *l* is for the teacher to move the jaw slightly downward, the lips drawn toward the corners. The *l* pattern does not permit a wide-open mouth, as the open mouth sets a pattern which will not be used later on, when *l* appears in speech; nor should the teacher open her own mouth wide when showing the visual pattern. An open space between the two rows of incisors, slightly more than is seen in the position for *e* as in "eat," permits the tongue to adjust to its required shape more easily than if the mouth is open and the tongue is straining to lift itself upward. The teacher uses thumb and finger of the other hand, on the upper jaw, at points from three-fourths of an inch to an inch apart, equidistant from the mid-line, to press steadily inward. This stimulation is directed to the tongue to induce it to move forward, not toward one point, but to broaden itself, fitting it to the curve of the dental ridge. The steady pressure tends also to stimulate a steady stream of air forward. Repeat this same stimulation a few times, and if no result ensues, drop it temporarily in a casual way, and return to it later on. When the sound comes, it will be the vowel beginning of the *l*; it should be sounded just long enough to be heard, as in normal speech, but it is necessary in order to produce the desired consonant ending sound afterward.

Second part in the stimulation of *l*: while the vowel-like beginning is sounding, by a quick firm movement of the hand which is contacting the lower jaw, move it downward, thus changing the nature and course of the current. The slowed-down picture of the air current permits one to think of the air molecules as being pressed outward at the sides of the tongue, through the two small openings, and then of the current being suddenly released from its course through these small openings, and disrupted, bringing the consonant sound of *l*, which immediately passes into the sound next to be stimulated. Thus two sounds are fused as in normal speech.

If the use of the air current dominates one's thinking, as one approaches speech training, certain adjustments as to the functioning of the muscles is more easily made. The requirements for the use of the air for a certain sound is primary. How the muscular functioning may most easily meet these requirements is another conditioning factor. Nature has definite ways by which muscles may best co-ordinate movements. If nature's plan for co-ordination may be utilized in the stimulations, the most comfortable and effective flow of movements occur. The usual pattern for co-ordinating muscular action for the first step in making the *l* sound seems to be to lift the tongue, to broaden the tip, and to adjust it to wherever it may move most directly to the dental ridge, since there is little forward pressure required. This usually brings the tongue end a little farther back than in the usual position of contact for the other tongue-end sounds. This position seems to be the pattern in the functioning of the average case. However, there are many gradations in the way in which individual habits are formed. There are tongues which lift the tip with difficulty. The student will bear in mind that the only requirement is that air be shut off in front. There are cases which get a fairly good *l* by bunching up the middle part of the tongue, and making this rounded part contact the part above while the point is dipped. Difficult cases may be led to close off the air by holding the tongue against the back or even the edge of the upper teeth. The appearance of the mouth is not as pleasing in this latter way, but the sound may be made satisfactorily unless there are spaces between the upper incisors which permit the escape of air there, to the detriment of its use inside.

Student practice for the sound of l, *followed by* a *as in "at."*—Stimulate the vowel part only of *l* when it is the final sound. Do not make the second part of the stimulation.

lap	left	lot	least	loaf	pull
lat	let	log	line	loose	fill
lad	led	light	loan	ball	old
lack	lend	lead	load	hill	soil

THE PRODUCTION OF THE *r* SOUND

The use of the air current as the *r* sound is made is similar to that just described for the *l* sound. In the case of the *r*, however, the opening through which the current is started is above the tip of the tongue. Usually, without contacting the dental ridge, the front of the tongue tips backward, so that the point looks withdrawn from the dental ridge. The sides of the tongue support this upward position, by holding close to the inside of the back molars. The vibrating air is forced through the opening which is formed between the tongue in the previously described position and the dental ridge. The opening is roughly crescent in shape. The opening at the lips is usually somewhat elongated from corner to corner; however, the lips do not need to move to produce the *r* sound. The first sound heard is vowel in nature. The next part, consonant in effect, is brought about by the quick movement of the jaw and tongue downward.

STIMULATION OF THE SOUND OF *r*

With the fingers of one hand, move the jaw slightly downward from a closed position. The lips are held unmoved with an elongated narrow opening between them. Since the usual substitute for the sound of *r* is the *w* sound ("wug" for "rug," etc.), the teacher keeps her hold on the lower jaw, not moving the lips but pressing slightly inward to prevent them from moving toward the middle. The same hold may be made on the upper jaw if the habit of movement toward the mid-line has already been established. Thus held, the lips cannot be used for the *r* sound. The subject is left no other alternative than sounding the *r* with the tongue, from inside the mouth. At times the vowel *r* comes forth with this partial stimulation, as the teacher sets the auditory pattern. If the attempted *r* is heard, the teacher moves the lower jaw downward while it is still sounding. The movement must be a very definite, firm one, so that a break from the first usage comes suddenly. Repeat the whole process a few times. If the result is not satisfactory, a repetition of the process later on will often yield better results.

The tongue depressor may also be used. Without opening the mouth wide, insert the depressor under the tongue, tipping the end backward slightly. Then try the outside stimulation. If the tongue does not lift easily, another way of securing the crescent-shaped opening is to place the tongue depressor over the front of the tongue, pushing the blade upward until only a narrow crescent-shaped opening is left between the lifted tongue and the roof of the mouth. This latter use is recommended only in cases where the tongue end lifts upward with difficulty, because of pathological conditions or a too long continued habit. Remove the depressor and continue with the outside stimulation. If the vowel beginning of the *r* is heard, but the consonant *r* is not heard as desired, it may be because the jaw, with the tongue, has not been moved away from the first functioning quickly enough. Consider what must be done to the air current to create this sound. Visualize, in a slowed-down picture, the current narrowed down to the small crescent-shaped opening, and the vocal folds functioning. The current, thus narrowed, must be broken up suddenly or the confusion created with resulting effect on the air particles will not be sufficient to make a clearly heard sound. A slow change in the action, permitting the current a gradual easing into the larger air stream, does not permit the formation of the consonant.

Let us start practice again, with *a* as in "at" and in "care" used with the *r* sound. The *a* as in "care" is stimulated in the same way as *a* in "at." (See Chapter Four.) But after the *a* is heard, without lifting the hand from the lower jaw, bring the jaw slightly upward from the *a* position, press inward, which may be sufficient to bring sound outward from the inside. The vowel beginning for *r* should be the result. As soon as it is heard, remove the hand, and do not stimulate further sound. If a final downward movement were stimulated, another vowel might be forthcoming, which does not belong to the spoken word "care."

Student practice for the r *sound:*

raf	wreck	rot	ride
rap	reg	rod	rude
rat	rel	rug	fare
rack	rig	rate	wire
red	rip	raid	pair

PRODUCTION OF THE CONSONANT *w* SOUND

The use of the air to start the *w* sound is brought about in normal speech by its being pressed through a restricted opening formed by the movement of the lips toward the mid-line. The sound of *oo* as in "food" would result if this position were held. However, it is not held longer than to start the sound. Then, with a quick movement, the lips move out of this restricted position, and the former course of the air current is upset. The consonant *w* is heard at this point of change.

STIMULATION FOR THE SOUND OF *w*

With the finger and thumb of one hand placed above the lips on the upper jaw, and the other hand placed similarly on the lower, bring the lips from the corners toward the mid-line, leaving an opening at the center. Sound *oo* as in "food." When the *oo* begins sounding, and while it is still sounding, move the lower jaw quickly into the position of the vowel which is to follow. At the same time, the upper hand reverses the former movement toward the center. This action breaks up the air current which is pressing toward a comparatively small opening at the lips and forces readjustment. The final activity to secure the *w* must be merged into that for the following vowel, so that the first two sounds may be spoken together, as in normal speech. The sound of the consonant *w* is used only as an initial sound. The letter *w* found at the close of words, as "cow," is a part of a diphthong, sounded as *ou* in "out." When stimulating a word like "worse," move immediately from the *w* into the vowel beginning of the *r* sound.

Student practice for the sound of w :

wack	wit	wall	wide
wag	wig	water	worse
west	will	wait	want
went	want	wade	woe
win	wash	weed	well

STIMULATION FOR THE SOUND OF THE CONSONANT *y*

The opening through which the air current is forced in this case is formed down the mid-line of the tongue, in the same way as for *e* in "eat." The sides of the tongue contact the dental ridge and prevent the escape of air there. Stimulate *e* as in "eat" as suggested in the chapter on the vowels. Give the auditory stimulation for *e*. Then move the jaw quickly downward, separating the tongue from the dental ridge in a quick movement. The consonant sound comes at this point. It sometimes helps to move the jaw, with the tongue, closer to the dental ridge, after the *e* is heard, then quickly downward again. Only the initial *y* is used as a consonant. If *y* ends a word or syllable, it is sounded usually like *i* in "it" or *i* in "ice," and will be stimulated as formerly directed for these vowel sounds.

Student practice for the sounds of y :

yap	yell	yale	boy
yam	yellow	yeast	baby
	(ye--lo)		
yet	yeg	year	bye
yes	yid	yost	try

CHAPTER SIX

SOUND SUBSTITUTION

The most apparent accomplishment during the first two years of the infant's life is gaining the control of muscular movements—movements of the arms, the legs, and the head, including the muscles of the mouth. The infant becomes conscious of his mouth, inasmuch as it is the means by which his hunger becomes satisfied. He also becomes aware of his mouth as a sounding mechanism, the means by which he may secure attention through making sounds. With normal vision and hearing, he sees and hears the mouths of persons around him, moving and sounding in speech. He attempts the same movements, since he has a tendency to imitate. He babbles, i.e., he moves his mouth muscles into various forms, and seems to feel a satisfaction in producing changing sounds.

While the infant's progress is apparent, outwardly, through increase in strength and complexity of movements, the inner processes are at work to bring about a certain degree of maturation, which enables the finer movements to start functioning. At this point of readiness, the infant usually starts the effort to turn his babbling into the words heard around him. His attempt often results in the use of the wrong muscles. This makes the sound incorrect. The infant's ear is not yet discriminating. Learning speech through the visual is also limited in scope, since it is not apparent how the adult makes all of his sounds. The speed with which adult speech movements proceed is also a handicap to visual aid in the child's learning of speech.

Hence, when left without definite help, a "trial and error" method is the only remaining recourse, as the infant changes from his babbling, step by step, into words. There would be no difficulty with such a beginning, were it not for the fact that the use of sounds to express meaning, repeated with that idea in mind, follows the law of habit formation, which tends to fix the movements for continued use. This is a very good thing, when the movements have been gained correctly, but is a handicapping thing when they are gained incorrectly, and have long-continued use. A tendency to continue the usage first learned interferes with movements which must replace them in correction, and the first forms are generally used for a period of time, the length of which varies in individual cases. If the first forms are gained correctly, each use thereafter strengthens the desired habit formation. By the same law, each incorrect set of movements becomes stronger with use. The first build-up may be an intricate interwoven set of habits, partly correct and partly incorrect, whose incorrect formations must be replaced before speech is correct. For instance, the use of the tip of the tongue, instead of the back of the tongue, will cause the infant to say "tum" instead of "come." The use of the lower lip, in-

50

stead of the tongue end, against the edge of the upper incisors, brings "froo" instead of "through." As just indicated, the use of the movements which normally produce one of the sounds of speech may be used for another. This use of one process for another results in *sound substitution*.

At five years of age, the mistaken process yields to correction more slowly, other conditions being equal, than at four. The four-year-old is slower to change than the three-year-old. The three-year-old yields more slowly than the two-year old. Even then correction is not as satisfactory as the correct learning in the first place, which is possible if the movements are being guided by a skillful teacher.

Common substitutions are:

t for *k*	"tan" for "can"
d for *g*	"do" for "go"
g for *d*	"god" for "dog"
t or *s* for *f*	"toot" or "soot" for "foot"
d for *j*	"do" for "jo"
w or *y* for *l*	"yight" or "wight" for "light"
w for *r*	"wun" for "run"
te or *th* for *s*	"tee" or "thee" for "see"
b for *v*	"bery" for "very"

The history of the usual case using sound substitutions runs something like this: The parent accepts the child's "baby talk" as normal and "cute" during the first two or three years, thinking it will be outgrown in due time, like last year's clothing; but when four or five years pass, and the child is still using "baby talk," the parents awaken to the fact that the speech is not coming out right through natural processes. Especially does this come home to them when some neighbor remarks, "Your little boy doesn't talk very well, does he? Now, my Jimmy . . ."

The child starts to school, and the teacher speaks of the speech problem involved. As an illustration, consider the case of this child in kindergarten. At the end of the school year, the principal called in the mother and advised that the child be kept in kindergarten for another year, to allow her speech to become "clear." The child had two sound substitutions: she substituted the *th* sound for the *s* sound, and the *t* sound for the *f* sound. Even two sound substitutions make the speech sound quite different from the normal. The mother was much disturbed. She made a remark very common in such cases, "My child never has been able to make these sounds. It seems impossible for her to do it." The simple fact is that the wrong set of muscles had been brought into play when the *f* and *s* words had been learned four years previously. The tongue-end action had begun the *f* words, and that habit had grown stronger and stronger with each passing month, instead of disappearing with the passage of time.

The child was co-operative and wanted to be helped. The teacher placed the child's lip against the upper teeth and asked her to blow, as she herself was doing, and when the air began to move outward, the teacher brought the lip and jaw downward into the *a* position, as in "at," and within a minute the pattern was found for saying "fat" correctly. "Why didn't someone show her that a long time ago," the mother asked, "instead of letting so simple a thing prevent her promotion with her classmates now?"

The mother's question is worthy of serious consideration in the light of the writer's experience. Somewhere between the ages of twelve and eighteen months, at some happy moment, the child's lower lip could have been moved upward against the upper teeth, or gums, and the pattern felt and started correctly for the *f* words. In the months to follow, the correct habit could gradually have been formed, thus preventing the difficulty which led to failure in passing the grade at the close of her sixth year.

Another interesting case that came to the writer's attention was that of a child four years of age. Her substitution was *th* for *f*. A "thunny thish" made the words sound quite different from "funny fish." The father was a surgeon who, immersed in his own specialty and practice, had taken the child for consultation to medical specialists in various cities. Nothing physically wrong was discovered by the doctors and, up to that point, the parents had not consulted any teacher of speech. When they did, it seemed incredible to them at first that the only difficulty was one of incorrect muscle functioning. It was simply that the tongue end had started movement against the upper teeth instead of using the lower lip, as *f* words were begun.

In another case, a mother took her child to a speech clinic five hundred miles distant and boarded herself and her child for a summer—breaking up her own home temporarily—just because of three sound substitutions.

Still another case is that of two sisters. The elder was four, the younger about two years of age. The older girl confused the *g* and the *d* sounds. She said "god" for "dog" and "do" for "go." The younger imitated her, but had other substitutions also. The parents brought their children to the School of Speech in order to talk over the question of their speech. The writer and the parents consulted, apart from the children, after hearing them talk for a while. The writer explained the mistakes involved, and suggested a few lessons to show the children how to use the back-tongue action for *g* and the tip of the tongue for *d*.

Since it is difficult for parents to believe that children who have passed superior mental tests could need any special help in speech, these parents hesitated to start anything which, as they felt, might make the children self-conscious or to feel inferior. They decided to wait for a while, but after a year they returned. The parents had decided at last to have the children trained in speech. And on arrival, as the older child spied a small black cocker spaniel, she exclaimed, "Look at that cute little black god!"

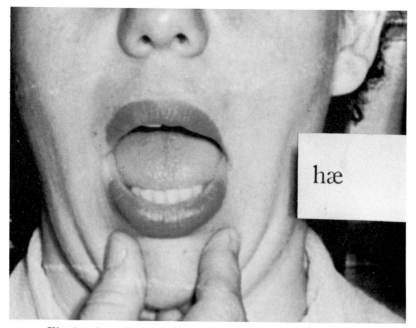

Fig. 1.—*ha* as in "hat" (hæ). Teacher moves lower jaw downward, ready for emission of air for *h*. Immediately, with other hand at waistline, she presses inward and upward to move the air outward in above position.

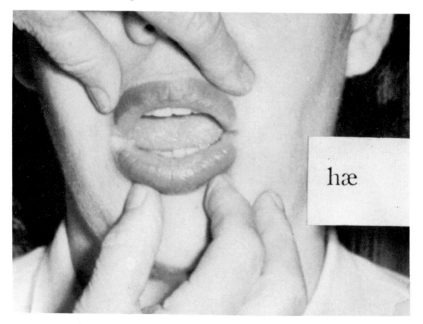

Fig. 2.—*ha* as in "hat" (hæ), continued. Teacher moves jaw upward from Fig. 1 to above position. Thumb and finger press inward following curve of lower jaw, tending to bring tongue behind lower incisors, for *a* as in "hat" (see Fig. 17).

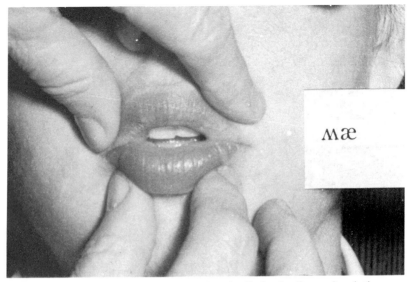

Fig. 3.—*wha* as in "whack" (ʍæ). Only the first stimulation is shown. The lips are being moved toward the mid-line, leaving an opening as indicated. The air is moved forcibly through this opening, starting the *wh* sound. To complete the pattern for *wha*, the hands reverse their direction of movement, into the short *a* sound (see Fig. 17).

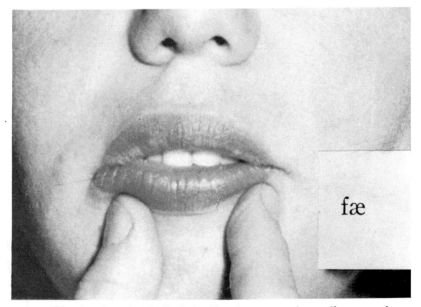

Fig. 4.—*fa* as in "fat" (fæ). Teacher moves lower lip upward and fits it to curved edge of upper incisors—beginning stimulation for *fa* as in "fat." Without lifting fingers, the lip and jaw are brought downward into the vowel position (not shown).

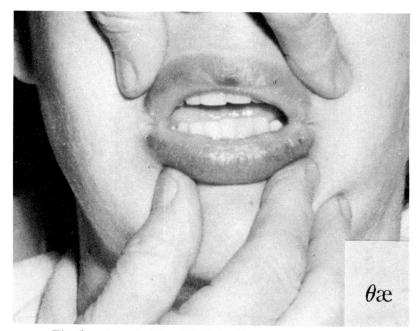

Fig. 5.—*tha* as in "thank" (θæ). Teacher places jaw and lips in above position, ready to stimulate tongue action (see Fig. 6).

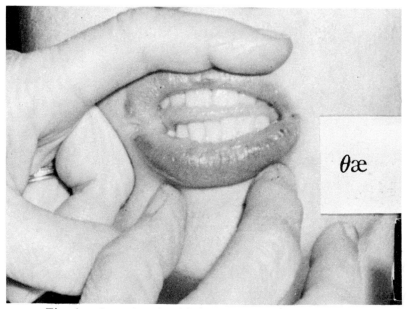

Fig. 6.—*tha* as in "thank" (θæ), continued. Teacher curves finger over lower part of upper lip, close to edge of upper incisors, and presses. Tongue tends to reach forward to line of pressure. Auditory and visual stimulations are made at the same time. As soon as air begins to move between tongue and upper incisors, bring jaw downward into vowel position (not shown here).

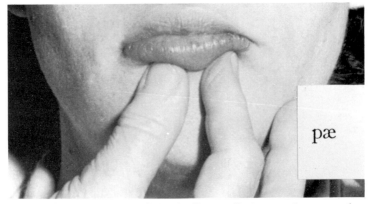

pæ

Fig. 7.—*pa* as in "pat" (pæ). Lower lip is brought upward to press against the upper, then is immediately brought downward, allowing emission of air, and is moved into vowel position (not shown here).

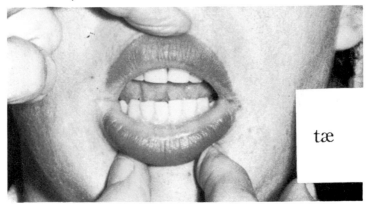

tæ

Fig. 8.—*ta* as in "tap" (tæ). Jaws are separated as above. Index finger is placed at midpoint of upper jaw. Finger presses, ready to move downward quickly—the cue to stimulate tongue action. Next, move lower jaw immediately downward into vowel position (not shown here).

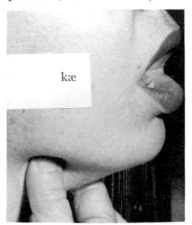

kæ

Fig. 9.—*ka* as in "cat" (kæ). Beginning stimulation—thumb and forefinger are placed on either side of throat at base of tongue outside. Fig. 9 shows the outer stimulation at highest point, fingers ready to come downward, to stimulate back of tongue to do same. Next move into vowel position (not shown here).

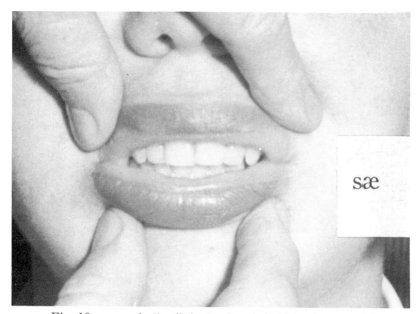

Fig. 10.—*sa* as in "sat" (sæ). Jaw is held in above position ready to move air down the mid-line of tongue between rows of incisors. Fig. 10 shows normal occlusion, normal functioning of joints. Thumb and finger on upper jaw press inward, and toward corners. As soon as air emerges between incisors, move lower jaw downward into vowel position to complete *sa* (not shown here).

Fig. 11.—*sha* as in "shall" (ʃæ). Lips and surrounding parts are moved forward and toward center, forming a scoop-like shape. Pressure is used on upper jaw as parts are moved. Air is moved outward while in above position. As soon as heard, move lower lip and jaw downward to complete *sha* (only the beginning is shown here).

Fig. 12.—*cha* as in "chat" (tʃæ). Mouth is moved into same outward position as for *sha* (Fig. 11). Pressure on upper jaw is more firm. Mouth is ready to sound *cha* as in "chat."

Fig. 13.—*cha* as in "chat" (tʃæ), continued. Pressure on upper jaw is removed. Lower hand moves jaw and lip downward, releasing air, and immediately into vowel position (not shown here).

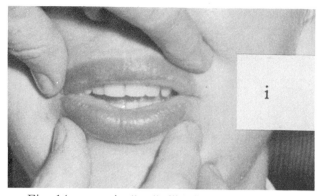

Fig. 14.—*e* as in "eat" (i). Lower jaw is moved closer to the upper, leaving small space between incisors, lips to corners. Auditory and visual stimulations are given simultaneously for *e* as in "eat."

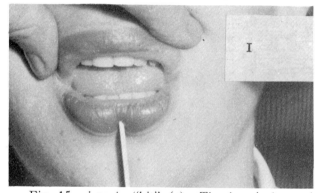

Fig. 15.—*i* as in "hit" (ɪ). The jaw is lowered slightly more than for *e* in "eat." Depression at midline of end of tongue is sought. Tongue end may be dipped, or pressure at mid-line below lower lip tends to dip tongue inside.

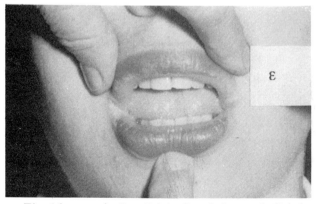

Fig. 16.—*e* as in "egg" (ɛ). Jaw is lowered slightly more than for *i* in "hit." Stimulation by pressure at mid-line point below lower lip tends to dip tongue end, and to bring sound forward to that midpoint.

æ

Fig. 17.—*a* as in "at" (æ). The jaw is lowered slightly more than for *e* in "egg." The thumb and finger on the lower jaw press inward and toward the corners, to make tongue feel curved row of lower teeth inside and adjust itself behind them, thus forming an inclined plane, down which the vibrating air passes outward.

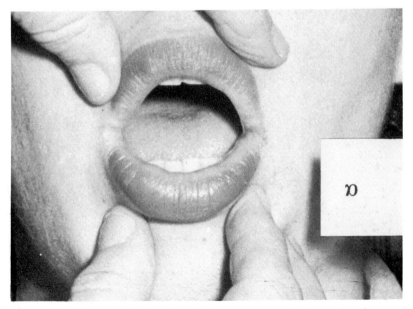

ɒ

Fig. 18.—*o* as in "top" (ɒ). Lips are brought forward as jaw is brought downward, approximately as shown. Teacher presses at the two points of contact on lower jaw. The stimulation for the back-tongue vowels is only partial. The outward placement of lips and jaw, done simultaneously with the auditory pattern, helps in achieving results.

Fig. 19.—*a* as in "all" (ɔ). Lower the jaw as shown, a little less than for *o* in "top" (Fig. 18). Lips and surrounding parts are brought forward.

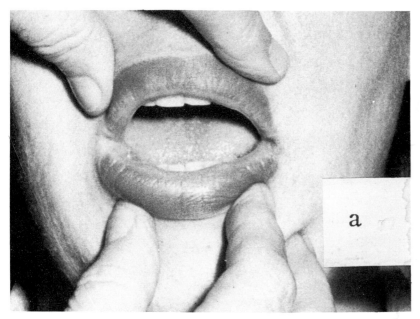

Fig. 20.—*a* as in "arm" (a). Jaw is moved slightly lower than for *a* in "at." Lips are drawn somewhat toward corners. Auditory pattern generally completes this partial stimulation. If not, dip central line with edge of tongue depressor.

Fig. 21.—*oo* as in "foot" (ʊ). The lips are being brought forward into a protruding position. The hand on the upper jaw does not press. The lower hand presses inward as it shapes the lower lip.

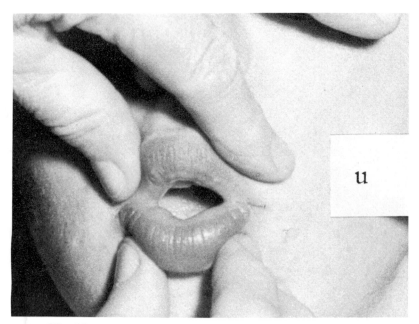

Fig. 22.—*oo* as in "food" (u). Lips are moved toward center, leaving opening as shown. Vibrating air moved through this opening tends to bring the correct sound. Auditory and visual stimulations are given simultaneously.

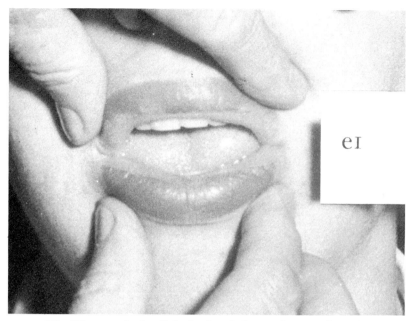

eɪ

Fig. 23.—*a* as in "ate" (eɪ). Jaw is lowered approximately as shown. Lower hand presses at points of contact. Next, both hands start moving lips to corners, ready for second sound of diphthong (not shown here).

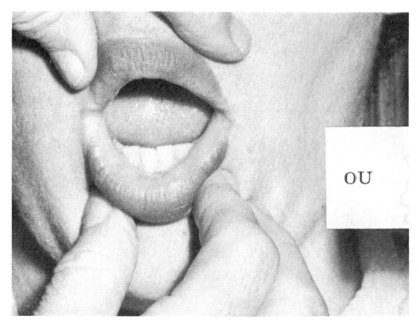

OU

Fig. 24.—*o* as in "oat" (oᴜ). The first placement of the teacher's hands lowers the jaw approximately as shown. Both hands immediately round the parts around the lips, then move into the *oo* position as in "foot."

Fig. 25.—*u* as in "use" (ju). Mouth is first shaped as for *e* in "eat."

Fig. 26.—*u* as in "use" (ju), continued. The thumb and finger on the upper jaw move from their first position, pressing against the upper jaw to bring sides of tongue against the dental ridge, and at the same time to bring joint action of lips to center, as for *oo* in "food."

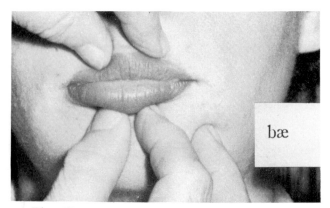

Fig. 27.—*ba* as in "bat" (bæ). Lips are pressed toward line of contact, starting *b* sound. Lips are separated quickly. The lower hand, keeping its contact, moves the jaw downward into vowel position, producing immediate *ba* as in "bat" (last position not shown).

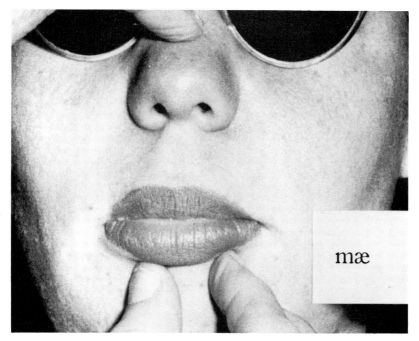

Fig. 28.—*ma* as in "man" (mæ). The hand contacting lower jaw brings the lower lip into contact with upper without pressure. Index finger of the other hand presses on the bridge of the nose. Upper lip is untouched by teacher's hand as *m* is stimulated. As *m* sound is first heard, move lower lip and jaw into vowel position to complete *ma* (not shown).

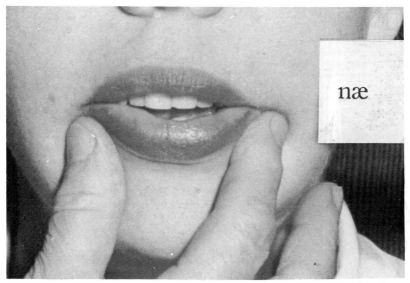

Fig. 29.—*na* as in "nap" (næ). To start stimulation, one hand keeps lips separated and toward corners. Index finger of teacher's other hand presses on bridge of nose, as in Fig. 28 (not shown in Fig. 29).

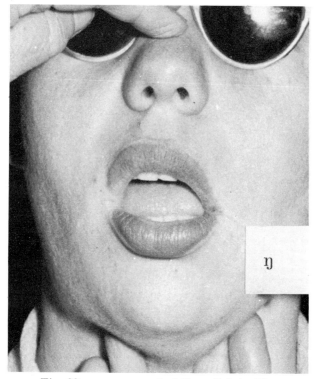

ŋ

Fig. 30.—*ng* as at end of "bang" (ŋ). Fingers contact throat lightly at base of tongue, and hold this position as index finger of other hand presses on bridge of nose to stimulate sound to move through nose.

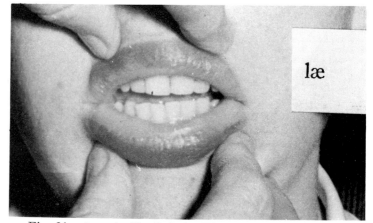

læ

Fig. 31.—*la* as in "lag" (læ). The lower hand holds jaw in position shown, and also keeps lips toward corners. Finger and thumb on upper jaw press at points of contact, to bring tongue upward. Give auditory pattern. As soon as the vowel-like *l* is heard, the lower hand moves firmly downward into the *a* position to produce *la* immediately (not shown here).

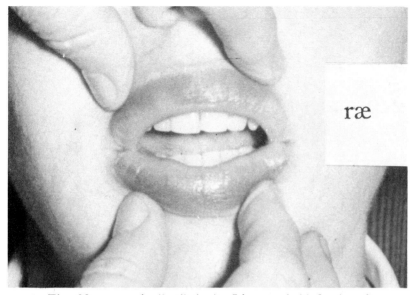

Fig. 32.—*ra* as in "rat" (ræ). Lips are held firmly, after tongue end has been tipped back with tongue depressor. Lips are held firmly to prevent *w* substitute. Lower hand is ready to move jaw quickly and firmly into *a* position as in "hat," blending two sounds. (Only first position is shown here.)

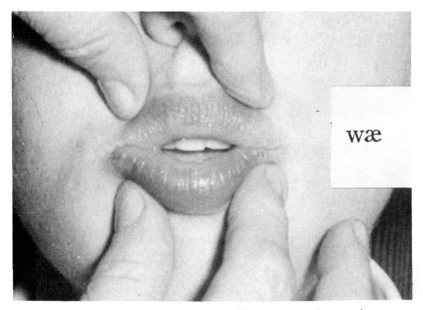

Fig. 33.—*wa* as in "wag" (wæ). Lips are moved toward center, leaving opening as for *oo* in "food." As soon as sound is heard, teacher reverses direction of movement. The lower hand moves into the vowel position—with continuous sound. (Only the first stimulation for *wa* is shown here.)

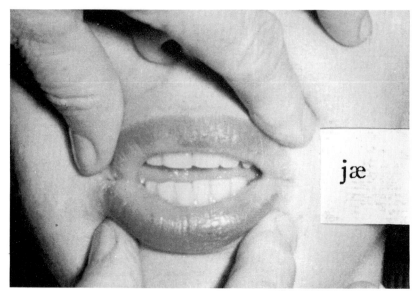

Fig. 34.—*ya* as in "yap" (jæ). Lips and jaw are first moved into the *e* position as in "eat." Thumb and finger are pressing on upper jaw. Lower hand moves jaw and tongue quickly downward and then into the vowel position (not shown).

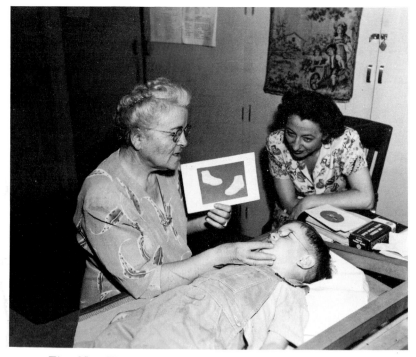

Fig. 35.—The child is shown lying relaxed on the "speech table" while the teacher stimulates "shoe." A student-teacher looks on.

The children were shown that when the mouth starts saying "dog," the tip of the tongue pushes to the front of the mouth. The teacher pressed at the mid-line outside, above the upper lip. Each child readily responded to the "do" stimulations and then the teacher placed her thumb and finger outside, at the base of the tongue, and the child got the *g* sound. Next the teacher took the child's hand, and showed her how her own hand could help her mouth to make the word "dog." The child pressed with one finger, at the front, and got the first two sounds of "dog," and then changed to the back-of-tongue stimulation for the ending. The child did this eagerly, and was happy to make her own correction. The teacher saw these children just three times, which seemed to be all that was necessary, as the older child learned how to help herself, as well as her little sister. Then they continued their practice at home.

It is true that the average child does correct such mistakes by the time he enters kindergarten. Some, however, do not find these corrections in time to prevent the force of habit from gaining too strong a hold through the constant use of the movements they first learned. Wherever this happens, correction in a factual sense means an injection of a different process, or processes, into an already automatically learned sequence of movements. This is true whether the child succeeds in making the corrections himself, or whether the teacher helps him to make it. In either case, the smoothest possible flow of speech is hindered, and time is lost through the necessity of correction.

If a teacher is helping to correct errors of sound substitution, the combination of appeals by all available senses makes the strongest impression. The sensing of the new process through kinesthesis, as directed by a skillful teacher, is a great aid in changing from the process already in use to another. The child should be led to make the change first in a simple word, usually at the beginning of a word, by feeling the correct stimulations, such as "cat," to replace "tat." The auditory pattern is given by the teacher simultaneously with the stimulations for movement. When the child is able to speak the one word correctly by himself, it should be practiced in combination with other words, as "my cat" or "Tom's cat," in which the mouth changes from various positions, into the new form which starts "cat." By degrees, the final and middle *k* sound may be worked into the practice, as "back" instead of "bat," etc. In correction, it helps to stabilize the correct sequence if the patient can *feel* the location of the substituted process, as he hears the correctly spoken word. It helps to remind the child of the correct form. This should be done casually, cheerfully, patiently, giving him *time* to overcome a previously formed incorrect use of his muscles.

The correction of sound substitution would seem to be one of the easiest defects to correct. The writer's experience would indicate that correction is not completed, not necessarily *ended,* when the child *sounds* as if corrected, when, for example, he has transformed "Me tan det it" into "I can get it" in daily use. Instability has become a part of the usual functioning. That is—to try to describe a factual personal experience— it is as if the directive from the motor area of the brain is now capable of producing two possible reactions in the peripheral muscles. An upset emotional state may cause the first learning to be attempted again, and confusion and the beginning of muscular conflict may result. The extent to which the first learning handicaps the individual seems to depend upon the child's background, neurologically and psychologically.

To summarize, sound substitution, a so-called speech defect, is one which could be prevented, or at least be minimized. It is usually caused by inaccurate learning, on the part of the human being, when he is too immature to find the correct use of the muscles of speech. The law of habit formation starts fixing these first-learned engrams, and continues its hold on such uses, until it becomes difficult to change. Some children correct baby talk more easily and earlier than do others, depending upon other conditions in their lives.

Correction of sound substitutions may be best helped by the child's *feeling* the new process to be substituted, while simultaneously hearing the correct sound. The correction is gained more easily through the moto-kinesthetic approach at an early age in childhood, since learning through moving and doing are gained largely through the effect of previously felt patterns.

Sound substitution, corrected early, frees a child from the consciousness of his speech later on, permitting him to give his whole attention to his growing interests, with the tools for expression accomplished, ready for use without the thwarting experience of having to change movements which have already become automatic through continued use. These common articulatory difficulties are not a defect, except that in the immaturity of infancy, the learning may be defective, and mere maturation of body and mind do not necessarily produce the normal development from speech of infancy to that of early childhood.

When the deciduous teeth give way to the permanent set, between two-and-a-half and six years, we often expect to call on the dentist for help and expert advice. In the same way, it often seems far wiser to straighten out the child's speech, in this early formative period, than to let habits persist until it becomes most difficult to change them. In this, an "ounce of prevention" is worth many pounds of advertised "cures" in adulthood.

CHAPTER SEVEN

DELAYED SPEECH AND SPEECHLESSNESS

The normal development of speech is dependent upon certain other forms of development—physical, mental, and emotional. Also, in a very important sense, environmental factors influence speech development.

Where there are so many interrelated factors to influence the speech-learning process, and where each must contribute a certain amount of normal functioning to enable the process to develop satisfactorily, it is to be expected that there will be variations in the speed and accuracy of the learning. If the child suffers a succession of illnesses, and if pain, weakness, and discomfort are continuous elements of daily life, the child will put little effort into speech learning at that time. If the first two years or more are spent in this way, the habit of satisfying daily needs is formed without the use of speech. Crying, temper tantrums, or rage may become habitual when the child cannot make himself understood. Laughter, in an exaggerated way, or an infantile up-and-down movement of the arms may become habitual patterns to express pleasure. If speech is delayed into the third year, because of illness, the child may become introverted, antisocial, emotional, indulging in frequent outbursts of feeling which have become his only means of expression during his various illnesses. Even if the physical health is restored to normal by three to four years of age, the natural urge to gain speech, as is normal in the earlier months, is often replaced by a negative attitude toward it, and toward all speech stimulation. The best time for beginning has passed. At this point there are two alternatives: the child may learn to speak, given careful help; or he may never find the way into speech, but may remain speechless or with only a few words, over a period of months or years.

Jimmy, for instance, was speechless at seven years of age. He had had measles at one and a half years. Previously he had babbled normally, but the normal babbling ceased as the measles attack came on. He had hardly recovered from this illness when he was stricken with scarlet fever. Recovery was slow. It was difficult to feed him and he cried a great deal. He developed tantrums when he could not make himself understood. At the age of four, his physical condition had greatly improved. Then his tonsils were removed. Still he did not talk. At the age of seven, he was continuing to express himself through protracted cries and similar sounds, but used no words. His gross muscle movements had become exaggerated, in his attempts to express himself. He had retained the infantile slashing movements of the arms, and often danced up and down when pleased or excited. In Jimmy's case, speech was ignored during his various illnesses. The parents expected it to develop naturally later on.

55

The writer has frequently supervised the speech development of similar cases, following various illnesses and childhood diseases. Except at critical periods of illness, we have found such children more interested in little speech games, in learning the names of objects and their uses, while convalescent, than when they are quite well and other interests have become paramount. Simple play with the child, such as a toy monkey, drawn up and down, creates interest for a moment. The mother says "Up!" and "Down!" as she pulls the strings. Soon the child is attempting to do the same.

The writer was in contact with another junior patient with a similar history. The mother had learned under direction how to stimulate the words which she felt the child should be saying. Slowly, between one and three years, speech was built up. The mother waited for the moments when the child wished attention, and was ready to respond to speech "play." By the fourth birthday, the speech was normal, health had been restored, and the child entered school, prepared to meet the challenge of his age group.

Jimmy's delayed speech, lasting to the seventh year, was due primarily to the physical condition, as was that of the second child mentioned. However, the relationship between various factors which influence speech, such as the physical, mental, emotional, and environmental, are so interwoven that each has its influence in the learning process. On the other hand, there may be some one dominant factor which exerts a primary influence on the appearance and development of speech. Where the physical condition is normal, environment is favorable, and the emotional life is secure, we have the best background for the acquisition of normal speech. If there are frequent or constantly disturbing emotional upheavals, these upset emotions tend to retard speech development and sometimes normal mental development, because under such conditions the child cannot give the necessary sustained attention needed for learning.

What any child becomes, emotionally, is dependent to a large degree on conditions in his environment. Each home exerts its own kind of stimulation, and no parents duplicate exactly what other parents do for their children. Parental relationships have much to do with the entire development of the child, even in learning to talk. If the adults have a harmonious relationship, and good feeling pervades the home atmosphere, it is communicated to the infant and becomes a factor in building up the right sort of stable emotional patterns for the child. This aids in normal speech development.

When parents have not found a happy mutual adjustment, the tensions which result become communicated to the child and create a sense of insecurity. The following is an illustration in point. A father and mother had discovered early in their married life that they were incompatible; they seemed unable to resolve their various problems. By the time their first child was born, a girl, they had come to the conclusion that their affairs had reached a deadlock. By the time the child was able to creep, they had agreed that the baby must not hear them quarrel. Conversation became tense and stilted. The parents were unhappy and could not give their child the good cheer and happiness which helps a child to develop normally. The mother rarely talked to the child, although she gave her the necessary physical care. Since she did not hear speech, the child did not learn the necessary auditory patterns, nor did she learn the meaning and need for speech in social intercourse, as the father and mother rarely talked in her presence.

Not approving of divorce, the parents felt that they should stay together despite difficulties. They managed to work out a better understanding by the time the child was four years old, but it came too late to save the situation for the child. At four, she was speechless. At six, she was still speechless, and her mind seemed undeveloped. Her emotional life was tense, disturbed, and uncontrolled. There was no apparent desire to learn to talk at that late period. After a series of tests, it was decided that the child should be placed in an institution for the mentally retarded. Yet, at two years of age, this child had been considered a normal infant by the pediatrician. Speech is not acquired in solitude, and with lack of speech no child can communicate satisfactorily with its kind.

We have found that in order to gain speech the child needs to hear speech, to observe its use, to understand the meaning of oral communication among people. While every child requires consistent, regular physical care for normal growth, it is also true that the good influence of happy people about him helps to free the emotions, as well as to create an atmosphere of love in which he is nourished and on which he thrives. Such a home gives a child a zest for living and helps him in maturing, however young. Normal speech development is the natural outgrowth of this kind of background, together with sufficient understanding of child care and training to accompany it.

The writer came in contact with a home in which there were two children, a girl of twelve years and a little boy of three years. The parents had wanted a son, and when he came their joy was unbounded. He absorbed the mother's full attention, and she was always wondering what she could do to please him. Even when the child was napping, the mother said that she would pick out the toy she believed he would like best, and place it where his eyes would light upon it when awaking. The mother left no room for the child to develop initiative; he was smothered with love, and became negativistic. When he should have begun to talk, he failed to do so, and at three-and-a-half this boy was speechless. On entering the Hill-Young School in Los Angeles, he was at first left to his own initiative and was not asked to talk. He was very much interested, however, in watching the other children as they had their speech lessons.

Within a week, he volunteered to climb upon the "speech table"[1] to have his own speech lesson, as he had seen the other children do.

A similar case was that of a child who had also been very much wanted, and for whom so much had been done that he had begun to dominate the household. Speech had not developed, and he secured all of his wants by the use of one sound—a demanding "grunt." Whenever members of the family heard this sound, they rushed to discover what was wanted. "Is this what you want?" was the query, as they pointed to one thing after another. If so, he responded by a grunt in a pleased tone. If not, the sound was louder and more unpleasant. This lad was like a king in the home, with everyone ready to act at his slightest bidding. His speech, though long delayed, became normal with help. He finished the public school curriculum, and later attended college. Such a delay in speech as his, when carried over into the third or fourth year, is much more easily overcome than when the delay is allowed to persist into the fifth or sixth year, or beyond.

Among causes for delayed speech, which we may consider primarily environmental, are the attitudes and reactions of members of the family regarding the child's speech. When delay begins to be recognized, the family is apt to show undue concern. As they become more and more aware that the child is not talking normally, they usually discuss it in his presence, making him self-conscious and less willing to attempt speech.

We have seen older persons laugh at the oddities of pronunciation of little children. One case was that of a child of four years who had numerous sound substitutions and who used certain words in which syllables were reversed. This boy's older brothers mimicked him and thoughtlessly held him up to ridicule. When the boy said "topato" for "potato," his brothers often burst out laughing, and the boy resented this treatment. Finally, one day when they mocked him with "Topato, topato. I want topato!" it seemed to be the last straw and the child stopped talking entirely. When the writer saw him, two years later, he was speechless. He had turned against all their efforts to get him to talk. Being proud and sensitive, he did not want to be ridiculed, and this was all that was necessary to cause the boy to stop talking; then, as time passed, he seemed really unable to talk, for lack of practice. Ridicule of children's speech should never be allowed. What seem to adults to be relatively unimportant episodes in home life, may have far-reaching and unforeseen results to a child. Being ridiculed or criticized constantly, and compared unfavorably with other children, tend to contribute toward a delay in speech.

A normal infant of two years was left in care of a Spanish-speaking

[1] A specially built table for the teacher's use, on which the child, in reclining position, may be helped in forming correct speech patterns more easily than when in an upright position.

nurse while the parents were employed during the day. Because the child was put to bed early, and the parents were too fatigued to play with him much at evening time, he heard very little English. He seemed to resent the presence of the nurse and her "different" language, which he did not attempt to learn. Consequently his own speech was delayed and he was speechless at the age of three-and-a-half years.

Another infant was placed in a back yard and left to amuse himself, as soon as he could walk, while the mother went about her housework. He had no playmates and, though he developed the larger fundamental muscles to an unusual degree, he was not talking at four years of age.

Another interesting instance of delayed speech was that of a child whose constant companion was her grandfather. She followed him about as he did the ranch chores, talking her baby talk to him. When the grandfather suddenly died, the child became highly emotional, and stopped talking. At six years of age she was still speechless.

In such cases, we would suggest that nothing be said to the child about speech at the time of unusual emotion, and that he not be urged to talk. Rather, he should be given the opportunity to rid his mind of the unfortunate memories or situations which caused him to be disturbed, and to direct his attention to other interests and situations which would divert him from his own unhappy state. If this is done, the child will usually take up speech again as the shock is forgotten, if no issue is made of speech at the time.

Although the native mentality of the child is a factor in speech development, a delay in learning to talk is not necessarily an indication of low mentality. The kind of intelligence, and the aptitude for one kind of learning rather than another, has a bearing upon the problem. Boys are usually slower in starting to talk than are girls, as their interests from the beginning seem to be centered on the use of the larger muscles. They usually compensate for their slower start, however, by three years of age. A boy of sixteenth months, whom the writer observed, could run fast without stumbling and throw a ball with great accuracy. His parents felt that he should be starting to talk, and often attemped to get him to imitate words. This always ended in his getting away from them, to engage in some larger motor activity. Later on, when speech had developed, mental tests showed that he was not only up to the average, but superior, in spite of a lack of early interest in learning speech.

We believe that with a different beginning for speech, many of the children so far described could have been aided earlier and, with no speech problem to hinder growth, could have enjoyed a normal development. We have seen children with speech delayed to two-and-a-half or three years who show the psychological ill effects of the lack of the power to communicate. We have also seen these same children progress normally, once they have learned to talk. Such a case was brought to our Hill-Young School in Los Angeles by a kindergarten teacher in a nearby nursery school. The child's difficulty had been declared purely psychological, and his teacher was convinced of this, as she said that he always isolated himself from the group and did not seem to know when he was spoken to, or to be aware of what was going on about him. She maintained that he often went into temper tantrums and was a misfit among other children. Since similar reactions had been observed among other speechless children, the Speech School recommended definite help first in speech training, to see if personality changes might not follow the socializing effects of speech. "But," exclaimed the teacher, "since he pays no attention when you attempt to teach him words, how can he be taught to talk?" However, it was decided to give him speech training for a trial period of a few months.

At the beginning of the training, the child was placed among a group of young children, who took turns ascending the steps of the speech table for a lesson. Using the defense mechanism of pretense, so common among speechless children, this child pretended not to see what the children were doing, turning his back to them and looking out a window. The speech teacher tried to think of some way of arousing the curiosity of the boy, and so stimulated the child on the speech table to say the word "cup," following the moto-kinesthetic method of directing the movements externally. The child on the table, cup in hand, said "cup." The teacher went on, in a playful attempt, "My! Such good milk! Would you like to drink it from the cup?" Immediately the child at the window turned to look toward the teacher, came and pulled the cup down, and looked inside. His curiosity had led him to see if there really were milk in that cup. Then he returned to his place at the window, apparently embarrassed at his own action. In a few days, when the teacher said, "Who will be next to climb the steps?" this boy was the first to volunteer. The teacher kept him only a moment for this first attempt, assuring him that he might come back another time. Daily lessons followed, and in three months the kindergarten teacher reported that he was a different child in behavior. His use of pretense was disappearing, upon his development of words. He was entering more fully into the life of the nursery school, and his development seemed assured.

Another similar case was that of a three-year-old boy, who showed the beginnings of severe psychic disturbance. He had been a sickly baby. The pediatrician had advised much outdoor life and rest, keeping excitement and confusion to a minimum. The mother had him sleep on the porch, tiptoed about, and attended to all his physical needs. She talked to him scarcely at all. In fact, she overdid the doctor's orders in her extreme caution and fearful interpretation of his orders. At three years the child was irritable and constantly demanding, through cries and tantrums. He was brought to the School of Speech, where he watched other children as they took their speech lessons. He soon became interested and manifested a desire to participate himself. He was in the school for twelve months. When he left, he was using words to make his wants known and had ceased to have tantrums, although he was somewhat irritable at times. It takes time to eliminate these firmly set emotional patterns. The important thing, to him and his family, was that with speech he was now headed in the right direction. Three years later, when the school again heard from the parents, this child was a healthy, normal boy, doing well in the second grade.

Another one of our subjects was a speechless girl of four years, whose main outlet was a shrill and sharp scream, used when she could not make her wants understood. After the first days of adjustment were over in the school situation, and rapport had been established, the speech teacher explained to the child that the teacher could help her to talk by showing her how to make these sounds herself, and that when she wished her mama to come, she could learn to say "come," as other children said it. The teacher then stimulated the sound of *k* in "come," also producing simultaneously the short *u* sound, or "kuh," followed by the lip movements for the *m* sound. The child co-operated, and in a moment was repeating "come" as the teacher repeated the stimulations. This incident made a lasting impression upon the writer, and she can still envision the smile which appeared on the child's face when she recognized that she had succeeded in saying a word hitherto unused. As new words were learned daily and directed by the teacher, they became associated with the ideas for which they stood. In the teaching, the objects named were always presented to the child's view, to associate them with the names taught. The child's cries became less and less frequent, as she found she could begin to use words as others do.

From the cases cited here, one may assume that the gaining of speech, as well as mental development, based partly upon speech experience, is not always inevitable with the passing of time. Even if a child is fortunate in physical development, there are often other conditions which are capable of delaying speech to an age when it comes less easily and naturally. Speech should be well begun by two years of age. Even if it is baby talk, it serves the purpose of communication and helps to prevent the damaging mental results which come with too long a delay in speech.

After watching the development of speech of young children for many years, the writer believes that the keynote to successful all-around development hinges largely upon the gaining of speech at the normal time and in a satisfactory manner. If there were no alternative but for speech learning to be left to the uncertainties of physical development, caprices of the emotions, and affective conditions within the environment, there would be no value in writing this volume; but since the writer and her associates have found that there is a surer way of aiding speech than leaving it to trial-and-error processes, she urges the employment of the direction of speech movements, the moto-kinesthetic approach, wherever the learning is slow or incorrect. This renders the development of speech surer, and prevents harmful delays and personality disturbances which are the usual outcome of delays in normal speech development. A new approach to speech, rather than to urge the child to "say" thus and so, may intrigue his interest, once he finds how to do it, as well as what to do, and how to glide from one sound to another without stopping. Speech acquisition is a most difficult mechanical process to be learned, and one which no child inherits full-fledged, as some adults seem to think. The child may turn against visuo-auditory approaches, when he has not succeeded in the act of imitation. Moreover, the exact pattern for the functioning of the various muscles involved may be acquired and set through a moto-kinesthetic approach, when the child will not respond to the visual or auditory methods in a normal way, at the usual time. He feels how the movements are made for various sounds and hears simultaneously the teacher speak the word; he senses a real aid to learning to say the word, and often responds with good effort on his own part, once he knows what to do, and how.

To summarize—whatever the cause or causes may be, if speech is delayed beyond the third year, and the delay is protracted, it tends to produce a disturbed emotional condition. The state thus fostered tends, in turn, to prevent mental progress, as energy is directed into emotional channels. Ordinary attempts to get the child to talk may arouse resentment or frustration. He may seem to deteriorate as compared with others of his age, or to be at a standstill; and if he continues without speech, the parents may even be advised to place him in an institution for the mentally retarded.

The specialists, who test such children at six or seven years or older, generally find them unable to pass the mental tests at their age level. They are often erratic and emotional, tending to repeat the same actions habitually, and to perform very limited tasks. They cannot meet the challenge of their age group mentally or emotionally, and therefore may fail to achieve mature independent living.

When the child has grown into the state previously described, it is too late to undo the past satisfactorily. A work of prevention is possible, however, to enable the child to make a normal development as he goes through the routine of living his early years, day by day. Too often parents are advised that "speech will come," and that there is no need for worrying about it. True, worry does not help the situation, but there are certain constructive steps which may be taken to prevent later difficulty. The first step is to recognize the beginnings of a delay in speech. The second step is to analyze the various factors mentioned at the beginning of this chapter as related to one's own situation. Is the physical condition satisfactory? Is the environment such that the child is receiving from it the things which an infant needs to develop happily—even, consistent love and a feeling of security, through controlled conditions? Does he hear enough speech of a simple sort, planned for his immaturity (not baby talk), so that simple auditory patterns are clearly presented, and not a confusion of patterns which result from hearing speech which is too complicated for his understanding and learning? Are there moments spent, in the course of the day, in associating words with the objects for which they stand? Is there an attempt made to force the child to ask for what he wants? If so, there is a *better, safer* way to induce speech. To force speech is apt to produce a negative attitude. Simply name objects in his hearing—name them very frequently—in a casual manner and wait for him to attempt the word, without pressure. This brings safer results by far than to resort to force or pressure. Lastly, in addition to the previous suggestions, a careful use of the moto-kinesthetic method may solve many a problem, and prevent serious delay in speech.

CHAPTER EIGHT

CLEFT-PALATE SPEECH

In the study of cleft-palate speech, it is necessary for the student to understand the physical deviations from the normal as a basis for his understanding of the remedial speech work to be done. References are given at the end of this volume to enable the student to get the background and facts regarding the conditions to be encountered in these cases, together with the therapies in current usage. The speech teacher cannot safely proceed to work first, nor alone, on these cases. The advice of physician and surgeon is paramount in cleft-palate cases, as in all cases involving organic difficulties. Only when the surgeon has completed his task in repairing the physical condition, and has given his consent as to the time of beginning it, may the work of the teacher of speech be safely begun. If the surgeon's work is over by the time the child has reached the age of two years or even less, it is not too young to begin to apply the stimulations of the moto-kinesthetic method, step by step, as with all young children. Use the stimulations for words as already outlined (with certain possible adjustments considered later in this chapter).

The student will have a better understanding of the speech needs of the cleft-palate case, as he considers them in the light of the two fundamentals upon which all speech is built. First, an air current capable of being moved outward, through either the oral cavity or the nasal chambers, according to the nature of the sound in question; the second fundamental is the use of definite muscular movements, which must conform as nearly as possible to normal processes, in order to bring about the required uses of the air for speech.

In order to keep a current of air moving through the mouth and out at the lips, when the sound calls for such usage, there must be no other opening through which it may escape. Therefore, there must be surgery or other satisfactory means by which the opening, brought about by the cleft, may be closed. There must also be a means by which the air may be directed and sent forth, through either the mouth or the nasal passages, in accordance with the constantly changing requirements of the sounds. The soft palate is used under normal conditions as a curtain, being raised to prevent the current from going through the nose, and thus forming a clear passageway for it to go through the mouth, or being lowered to allow the air to pass through the nasal passages, as nasal sounds occur in speech. In the process of closing the cleft, then, there is also the need of keeping this soft-palate curtain in as usable and pliable a condition as possible. Surgery meets this need, as it closes the cleft, by giving especial attention to producing as normal a soft palate as the conditions will allow. Varying conditions in the mouth, nose, upper jaw, and lip produce a

64

variety of results, after surgery has completed its part of the task. Speech training is then indicated—is, in many cases, imperative—if understandable speech is to be achieved.

The training for postoperative cleft-palatal speech improvement requires not only a knowledge of the definite movements of speech and how to stimulate them, but also how these movements may be made to co-ordinate with the facial movements, to bring about the best results from the standpoint of appearance, and facial expression. We shall say more later on in the chapter as to how this co-ordination may be made effective.

REASONS FOR THE SOUND OF CLEFT-PALATE SPEECH

We have seen that the voiceless consonants are produced by pressing the air current through the mouth, under varying conditions, without the use of the vocal folds. The child who learns speech before surgery is done cannot keep the air moving through the oral chamber, because air escapes through the cleft into the nasal chambers. Therefore, the pattern for producing the voiceless consonants cannot be carried out successfully. For instance, the usual pressure of the air current toward the tongue end, ready to escape as the tongue moves downward to produce the *t* sound, cannot be exerted wherever a cleft exists. Pressure attempted sends the air through the opening. Sounds involving resonance through a chamber of certain shape and proportions cannot be produced correctly because the air chamber is defective and "leaky."

The child ceases to try to make the usual movements, because of the ineffectiveness of the results; but he must talk, if possible, in order to communicate. He may, therefore, do the only thing which his condition permits him to do—he may break up a possible continuity of sound into parts, simulating words in the rhythm of usual speech. His attempt at speech sounds nasal. If the cleft is not closed until the child has formed his speech habits, these habits, as first formed, tend to persist in the child's speech even after the opening is closed. The writer has heard parents complain that the operation was a failure, because the speech remained the same as before the operation. However, there is this important difference. *Before* the cleft is closed, it is impossible to bring about the necessary normal uses of the air current. *After* the closing of the cleft, it *is* possible to bring about these usages, through training. In such cases there are many detailed changes necessary in muscular movements. That is the reason for the urgency in using all possible helps available. The writer has found in some cases that immediate assistance is possible, in making these changes, by giving the patient the *feel* of the right functioning for a certain sound. The firm holding of the lip, for instance, against the edge of the upper teeth makes the subject conscious of the line of contact to which he must move the air, as he starts his *f* or *v* words. The practice of blowing the air through the mouth, as is done in inflating balloons, helps, but the definite use of the muscles, as is required in normal speech, must also be learned. The feel of the teacher's hands on the lower jaw, moving it firmly into the various vowel positions, tends to bring air and sound lower down, that is, through the mouth rather than through the nose. In other words, as the teacher stimulates each sound, its correct placing and production are felt, and thereby the learning process is aided and hastened.

As the cleft is closed through surgery, and if the two sides of the aperture are brought together, there may be a sense of drawing toward the mid-line, which sometimes influences the movements of parts around the mouth and nose. This is especially true if there is also a harelip. The training as given for sounds, words, and sentences in previous chapters may be used, and adjusted to the needs of the case, with additional training of the facial muscles.

There are certain possible variations, when moving the muscles to stimulate a few of the sounds, which it is well to keep in mind as one tries to bring about co-ordination between speech movements, and those for facial expression, especially for smiling. A ready smile is one of the best assets in making human contacts, therefore speech movements should be so directed that the outward moving action which produces the smile may be made easily from any and all positions of the mouth in speech.

Reflex action, which generally produces the smile as a reaction to a happy inward state, is often thwarted in the irregularities of the cleft-palate condition. It can be aided, however, by a teacher who learns how to direct it. For instance, if the mouth has completed the word "me," and if the person is about to smile at this point, the smile is simply the same position extended further outward and equally on each side.

In training for words containing the sounds of *th*, *t*, *k*, *d*, *g*, *s*, *l*, *n*, consonant *y*, *z*, *e* as in "eat," *i* as in "it," *e* as in "egg," *a* as in "ate," *i* as in "ice," the teacher may stimulate the lips as for normal speech, away from the mid-line to various distances from the corners, depending upon the sound in question. In stimulating words ending with these sounds, she may, at times, continue the outward movements, working for a symmetrical smile in cases of asymmetry. Of course, she might also say something provocative of a smile, so that the feeling of the smile could be associated with the balanced pattern being trained.

The following sounds require movement away from the corners, toward the mid-line, more or less according to the sound in question; *wh*, *sh*, *ch*, *oo* as in "foot," *oo* as in "food," *o* as in "oat," *ou* as in "out," *w*, *zh*, and *j*. These sounds should not be permitted to determine the habitual appearance of the mouth, but should yield after usage to the more elongated look, which usually permits better co-ordination of muscles around the mouth and the nose, and creates better co-ordination of movements for an equilateral smile. The adjustment of the lower lip to the edge of the upper teeth for *f* and *v* sounds is not always done so as to bring about the best co-ordination between speech needs and use of facial muscles, so as to function in a pleasing way. In directing the movements for these sounds, there are two different ways by which the lower lip may be brought into contact with the upper teeth, with many possible variations for each. The lower lip may be brought straight up against the upper teeth with the teacher's thumb and forefinger pressing toward the mid-line and up, giving the mouth a shorter, more concentrated appearance. Or the lower lip may be moved away from the mid-line toward the corners, and directed along the curved edge of the upper teeth, for a longer space, thus utilizing the same pathway as that used for the start of the smile movements, with the possibility of better co-ordinations. How the latter plan works may be shown in stimulating the word "leaf," in which the mouth is moved into the *e* position following the *l* sound, and then the lips drawn a little closer into the corners, as if ready for smiling, and up at the same time to contact the edge of the upper teeth for *f*, instead of a return movement toward the mid-line and up to the edge of the incisors. By this latter plan the region around the nose and upper lip may make a better appearance, when these uses become habitual. Usually there should be no movement of muscles of the nose itself, if the best means are used for co-ordinating the movements for speech and facial expression.

Facial distortions may mean that there is an effort to help speech by the use of the wrong set of muscles. This is sometimes lessened by helping the child to co-ordinate effort elsewhere, as in the muscles controlling the air from below, and relaxing the effort in the facial muscles. These muscles should be used symmetrically, or trained as nearly alike as possible on both sides of the mid-line. Sometimes, in blowing games, a child will be observed tensing and distorting the use of his facial muscles in an effort to blow with sufficient force. While he may be succeeding in forcing the air through the mouth, he is also forming habits in his facial muscles, which might prove to be displeasing with continued use.

Where there has been a cleft in the palate, there is often malformation in the shape and placement of the teeth, requiring help to find the best adjustment of the jaws to each other in speech. A trained teacher is in a better position to find these adjustments than to leave the matter to "trial and error" or to habit built upon chance efforts.

Generally considered, the movements of the jaw should be in a straight line, up and down, as this is the natural way for using the joints which control the jaw. A one-sided movement of the jaw gives a feeling of discomfort and imbalance in talking.[1] A jaw brought forward, out of line with the natural use of the joints, should be avoided if at all possible. One of the first things to be considered is how to bring about a close adjustment of the lower teeth to the uppers, leaving just enough space between the rows, so that they do not strike at any point as the jaw is moved up and down. This close position will be the one to be trained, as *s, z, sh, ch, zh,* and *j* come into the sequence. The movement of the jaw

[1] This was the writer's personal experience.

for the rest of the sounds is apt to follow the natural use of the joints, if the preceding sounds are trained to do so.

When the teacher has determined the desired movements of the jaw to be trained, she may then adjust the stimulations for sounds, as already given, to the case in hand. With irregularities to be considered, the main question is: How can the necessary uses of the air current be brought about, under these conditions, so as to permit muscular co-ordinations to function in as natural and as pleasing a way as possible?

In cases of great irregularity of the teeth, the advice of dentist, orthodontist, and possibly surgeon should be kept in mind. When training is being considered, there are many minor conditions which affect speech; for example, a lad of six was using back-of-tongue movements for all consonant sounds. In such cases, the student teacher may look for possible reasons for a tongue to withdraw from the frontal activity. The reason was quickly found in this case, when the teacher examined the front teeth. The lower incisors pointed backward, and had sharp edges, which the end of the tongue could not contact without real discomfort. An orthodontist was recommended, who started the work immediately to bring the incisors to a normal position, but who also ground off enough of the sharp edge to permit the training of the tongue to go forward, for *t, d, n,* and *l.*

Another case was that of a boy with a lateral lisp and one-sided movements for all of his speech. His smile was also one-sided. In this case there was a large misshapen molar, which had bent inward and grown into the mouth cavity, not leaving room enough for usual tongue activity. The teacher consulted a dentist, who decided to pull the tooth in question. Then, in time, the retraining brought normal speech.

Another case was that of a little girl who had not made the sounds of *sh, ch, zh,* nor *j.* A very small tooth was found projecting downward into the mouth, back of the dental ridge, at the mid-line of the mouth. The necessary closeness of the position of the surface of the tongue to the dental ridge for these sounds was impossible; the tooth came in between them. After the tooth was pulled, the sounds in question were made possible.

An adjustment often necessary, to bring about a better sound of *s,* might be illustrated by another example. The cleft in the palate had been successfully closed. The teeth were irregular, with large spaces between them. The help in this case was obtained by training the sides of the tongue to hold closely against the dental ridge, so as to permit no air to escape on either side. To this end, pressure was exerted on the upper jaw, outside, over the area where the sides of the tongue were expected to contact the dental ridge. The mid-line of the tongue was also depressed in training with the edge of a tongue depressor, to form the small pathway along which the air might move for the *s* sound. The sides of the tongue were also pressed firmly against the dental ridge with a portion of a tongue depressor. The jaw was moved to a position as nearly closed as possible without striking the teeth together. A good *s* resulted, as repetition of the whole process continued.

In closing this chapter on organic difficulties, the writer lays emphasis on starting training earlier and continuing for a longer period of time than is usually given to such cases. Under intensive training, where incorrect habits have been formed before the operation, there are postoperative cases which attain a satisfactory degree of improvement in a comparatively short time. Then the patient may feel that, since he is making himself understood, an effort to improve his speech is no longer needed. He may become unaware of the sound of his speech, thinking only of what he wishes to express in thought or feeling. In the long-range picture, there are postoperative cleft-palate cases which deteriorate in speech with the passing of time, or which may not achieve the best possible results because they stop effort too soon. The home phonograph, recording the speech from time to time, to permit the subject to evaluate his own improvement, might be helpful in some cases.

The individual may wish to escape from all thought of his former difficulty. To such a person, daily practice may mean a recall of former unpleasant experiences, which he wishes to avoid. However, to him who will persist untiringly in keeping his speech at its best level, checking it often, improvement will come gradually, and deterioration will be prevented.

CHAPTER NINE

SPEECH OF THE HARD-OF-HEARING AND THE DEAF

The auditory sense has always assumed a place of primary importance in the learning of speech, and also in the understanding of spoken words. Before speech training begins, a physical examination is important. The speech work should be done in consultation and collaboration with a reliable otologist.

Today the scientific study of hearing difficulties is being emphasized as never before. Whatever residual hearing is present in a case is being utilized through the use of better hearing aids. To the extent to which these aids bring the capacity to hear, the auditory sensations may be utilized and associated with the visual and with the patterns for movements as directed by another and felt through the kinesthetic sense.

It is not easy for those who work with the hard-of-hearing and the deaf, and who are not acquainted with our specific moto-kinesthetic techniques, to realize the benefit which is possible when the teacher has gained a skillful use of these methods of stimulation. The writer may state, however, that those teachers of the hard-of-hearing who have learned these techniques report that by co-ordination of the use of the methods which they had previously used, with the moto-kinesthetic stimulation, there is added help in many cases, especially with the younger children. Lacking hearing, there remains the visual sense and, even more effective in learning speech, the kinesthetic or muscular sense, when a pattern is given for the child to reproduce. Also, in a lesser degree, the tactile sense aids.

Through the visual sense, the child perceives the meaning of communication among people. He sees a mouth perform a series of movements. Another mouth responds, and answers the first. He then observes that people secure what they want as a result of mouth action. He gradually sees that certain mouth movements occur each time when a given object is designated. The help through the visual is limited, however, because the observer cannot see all of the movements which occur inside the mouth of the speaker, nor through sight can he sense the pressure essential at given points. Help should come from other available sources to supplement the visual picture which, by association, makes the reproduction of an entire process possible. The best help comes through stimulation to feel each process which produces a sound. The learning gained through trial and error is not as satisfactory as having the process stimulated by one who is skillfully trained. Through trial and error, various attempts are made by the child to find the correct pattern, thus bringing to the kinesthetic sense a confusion of patterns for learning, instead of one clear-cut definite pattern of action on which to build speech habits.

If a teacher is preparing to teach those who have a hearing loss, she should practice envisioning the definite uses of the air current, as presented in Chapter One, and then study the exact uses of the muscles which normally make these changing uses possible. This is followed by the study and practice of the stimulations which tend to produce each process. Then she will be in a position to stimulate the correct pattern for the kinesthetic sense to follow. The task of the kinesthetic sense seems to be to learn movements as they are used by a given set of muscles. It seems to have no power, however, to differentiate between right and wrong patterns. Correct learning seems to be thwarted when the child, through various attempts, changes his patterns. Confusion results, without that definiteness of learning which is so important. We might compare the effect of the various attempts to say a word to the result of multiple exposures on the sensitive plate of a camera.

The child without hearing is just as capable of sensing the patterns for correct muscular activity, through the kinesthetic and tactile senses, as is the child with hearing. The hard-of-hearing have the capacity for sensing the stimulations which are applied by the teacher, and which tend to produce normal sounds, even if not heard. Particularly is this true if started early in the life of the child, and the building of speech habits proceeds correctly, step by step, through the years of acquiring speech.

In the training process, two factors seem basic. One is a growing awareness of an outward moving air current, to be used when stimulations for certain sounds are given. The child may be led to feel this outward moving of the air used in the various ways which produce the voiceless consonants, by holding his hand before his teacher's mouth as she forms them. Again, he feels the vibrations which come as he contacts his teacher's face or throat, as other sounds are made.

Some sort of physiological sensing by contact has always been used by teachers of the hard-of-hearing and the deaf. This idea is not being presented as anything new in therapy. The writer does, however, urge a synthesis of all methods previously used successfully, with the added learning which comes through the stimulations of the moto-kinesthetic techniques, because these exact "patterns" are a composite, formed by directing location of the muscles to act in correct order, showing where to move, giving stimulation for the direction of movement, or how to co-ordinate several directions of movement into a desired whole-word pattern. Patterns of stimulation also include degree of pressure or tensions needed to produce certain sounds.

These stimulations should be performed in definite timing, to give the sound of normal speech. Therefore the teacher's stimulation is definite as to timing. These four factors form the background and basis of the application of the moto-kinesthetic work to the hard-of-hearing. Along with each word pattern sensed goes the necessity to determine whether or not each sound is vibrated, or whether it is felt only as a current of air blowing outward on the child's hand, if voiceless.

The next step for the student teacher to learn is the exact details by which she may train a mouth to move directly from one sound into another. The exactness of this stimulation determines whether a word may be spoken as a whole, fused together, or as a series of intermittent sounds. While it is important for all who would apply the moto-kinesthetic method of speech training to stimulate correct patterns of movement, it is more necessary for the patterns applied to the hard-of-hearing and the deaf to be correct than for any of the other groups, since they may not be able to check their results with any auditory pattern. The teacher or parent who will take the time, and make the effort to learn the stimulations finds a reward in the effectiveness of her results. But before she tries to use the techniques on any subject she must learn the stimulations and practice carefully with some other adult until the use of her fingers comes easily.

It is very important to start the stimulations early in the life of the child to get best results for later speech. If the teacher or mother is prepared ahead of time, she may, under ordinary conditions, begin this work with careful application of the techniques at least from the twelfth month on. Taking one word at a time, she may illustrate by moving her own mouth how certain movements of her mouth stand for the object which she is naming. The mother's or teacher's mouth activity should not be exaggerated, thinking that the child must *see* what she does for the whole word. What cannot be seen in normal speech will be learned when the pattern is stimulated, and the association of what can be seen must become associated with the feeling of the muscular pattern, so that each may become an aid to the other.

Let us consider the case of a hard-of-hearing child of twelve months. The mother has learned the stimulations for enough words to make a start toward speech. The first words should be names of familiar objects, such as "foot," "cup," "pin," "top," etc. Whichever one of these words is taught first, the next one should vary the appearance of the mouth in its beginning movements. The word "foot" shows the lower lip in contact with the upper teeth. The mother holds the child's hand in front of her mouth, so that he may feel the air blow out as she starts "foot." She also touches the child's own foot to indicate the meaning. When the right opportunity offers itself, she moves the child's lower lip upward and contacts the edge of the upper teeth, or gums. That is enough for one lesson. Only "foo," the first two sounds of "foot" (blended) are stimulated in the beginning effort. Then, later on, the stimulation for *t* may be added. The appearance of the mouth for "cup" is enough different from "foot" that the child may soon recognize the different meanings involved when the mother says *foo* and when she says *cu*, placing her head so that he may easily see her mouth. When the word "pin" is stimulated, he will feel a definite upward moving of his lower lip to contact the upper lip, moving downward immediately. His hand can feel the quick puff of air as the word "pin" starts. As the mother moves her mouth from the *p* into the vowel, she can place the child's hand on her cheek or throat, in order to sense the vibrations which come with the sounding of the vowel. Gradually he will learn to respond to this kind of stimulation also. The value of beginning early is that many mistakes may be avoided by learning the correct patterns in the first place, which use will strengthen into habit as time passes.

If the names of familiar objects are thus learned early, the child can make known many wants by saying single words. "Bread," "milk," "cup," said at two years, help him to express himself and tend to prevent emotional strain. Then, as time passes, the "I want" stimulations and "I see" help further expression. The commonest action words, like "walk," "run," "fall," "eat," may be included in later stimulations.

If the child is led gradually and carefully into the moto-kinesthetic training, the time will come when sequences for whole sentences may be stimulated and felt in detail and reproduced as the need is felt. When the cat stands looking at the child's mother, meowing eagerly, mother may stimulate, "Kitty wants milk." As the cat laps up the milk, she may stimulate, "Kitty drinks milk." When the cat jumps to the couch, "Kitty jumps up," and then, "Kitty jumps down." This vivid application of words to an actual situation should continue through the three- and four-year-old period. One should not correct too many mistakes, at one time, but should stimulate the same patterns again upon similar occasions. Prepositions and words which carry no clear meaning in themselves may be stimulated gradually, and felt in the normal sequence of movements. Sentences like "Kitty plays with the ball" may be stimulated in entirety, thus training the muscles for similar uses of the preposition. This may seem like unnecessary effort at the time, but if your child should fail to have usable speech at ten years of age, you cannot then turn back the calendar to give him a second chance as good as Nature's own best time for learning speech. Nor is satisfactory speech liable to develop if begun in those later years; the best years for fixing the definite patterns of movements for speech are then past. To make the best possible use of the first four years could mean satisfactory speech development in many cases which do not today develop speech because training has come too late.

While many children who have a severe hearing loss do develop speech by watching the mouth movements of mother or teacher, it is not necessary to depend so largely upon the visual alone. The task is too great, and often too discouraging. Those subjects who do succeed in the mastery of language, in spite of their difficulty, will be found to have had some devoted person, mother, or teacher, who sticks persistently to the daily teaching and inspires the child's effort and desire to learn and to want to improve his situation. Now, if the parent or teacher will use both approaches, through the visual and the moto-kinesthetic techniques, by starting with a step-by-step procedure from one year on, we may expect much better results in speech for the hard-of-hearing. The results may not be much in evidence during the first year of training, but the cumulative effect is apparent later on. *Results come in time.*

The mother or teacher who finds it difficult from these written pages to understand the meaning of the moto-kinesthetic techniques as applied to the hard-of-hearing and the deaf, is urged to start learning just a few of the stimulations, as described in earlier chapters. She should watch her own mouth in a mirror, as she makes a word. This will help to interpret the stimulations. She should do the necessary practicing on some other adult. If possible, she should work with someone who has already learned the stimulations and how to apply them. Through learning and doing, she will grow to know the value of these techniques to the world of hard-of-hearing and deaf people. We might add also that this is the only way the method will ever become of help to these needy groups. The process of learning by doing is preferable to reading about this method, because doing is concrete and definite, whereas reading about it becomes too abstract and vague. Its meaning is often lost to the reader.

TO PREVENT DETERIORATION OF SPEECH

Before concluding this chapter on the application of the moto-kinesthetic method to the speech of the hard-of-hearing and the deaf child, we should give some attention to another group which this method can help. These are the adults who lose their hearing through illness or various other causes, after reaching maturity, and with years of normal speech and hearing behind them. The speech habits may remain unchanged for a while after their loss, but since they themselves are unable to check their speech through hearing, deterioration in some of the sounds may occur. For instance, in producing the "s" sound, the close position of the lower jaw to the upper may gradually become relaxed, until the clear-cut sibilant sound may deteriorate in quality. One such case was that of an adult who had lost his hearing in middle age. Within a few years, his formerly clear-cut speech had deteriorated, making close attention necessary on the part of the listener in order to understand him. His jaw had fallen from its former close position as related to the upper, and so the sides of his tongue were failing to keep the air to the mid-line depression, as is necessary for the normal *s* sound. Where hearing is no longer a guide, the feeling of the position of the jaw at its former placement, is a very strong factor in keeping the *s* sound normal.

In another similar case, the processes for making the sounds of *b* and *m* had become confused. Not hearing the sounds as formerly there had gradually come about too great a pressure of the lips together, when some of the *m* sounds came in speech, especially when the speaker expressed himself forcefully. This man said, in talking to a group, "Too many *billions* are being spent," meaning *"millions."* As he said the word, he made an emphatic gesture with his right hand, which brought the two lips together firmly, producing the use of the muscles required for the *b* sound, instead of the *m*. Later it was suggested to him that he practice, bringing his lower lip against the upper with only enough pressure to keep the air from passing out between the lips, so that it might be sent through the nasal passages. The pressure on the bridge of the nose helped him, he said, to direct the *m* sound there, while consciously preventing undue pressure on the lips. After sensing the two processes carefully, followed by the practice of stimulations for words beginning with each of the sounds, he was able to produce either one as needed, with more of a feeling of certainty.

The *d* sound, which requires forward pressure of the tongue against the dental ridge, may gradually lose some of its forward pressure, as years pass, without the constant check which comes almost unconsciously with normal hearing. One such case was able to restore her normal *d* sounds by frequently pressing at the mid-line outside her upper jaw, with the same intensity which her teacher used in stimulating a pattern for a *d* sound.

To sum up—a teacher who thoroughly learns the stimulations for speech patterns may help the patient to understand the weaknesses in his speech which need attention. He may be shown how to keep speech functioning normally through the feel of a mechanical process, as stimulated by one who knows how, thus working for the prevention of speech deterioration in cases of severe hearing loss. This idea is not theory. *It can be done!* It has been done! It only awaits the acceptance of the *idea* to be carried out through practice and application.

CHAPTER TEN

THE BLIND AND THE DEAF-BLIND

As in the case of those who suffer from auditory losses, one finds that there are all gradations in the amount of loss which may be incurred in vision. Those who see well enough to discern the movements of the mouth are in a position to learn speech as the normally sighted do. Those who have no sight may not even realize where speech originates. One boy, who attended a nursery school for the blind, discovered through his teaching that speech comes with the movements of the mouth. "But," he said, "you weren't talking with your mouth when I first came to the school." In other words, he did not know how speech was produced until he was being taught to talk. Then he touched his teacher's mouth, and found for the first time how speech comes.

The blind child gains his knowledge of the outside world not only through hearing, but also through his finger tips. He touches everything. He learns to recognize familiar objects around him by their shape, size, and by certain attributes which he may sense through touch, such as hardness, smoothness, roughness, and the like. He feels the cat's fur, runs his hand over its contours, feels its head, ears, back, tail, and feet. He senses the movements of the cat through his sense of touch. The kinesthetic and tactile senses become acute, and help him to compensate for loss of vision. The blind child, because of his dependence upon feeling sensations, is conditioned to learn speech through the feel of the teacher's stimulations, as she associates them with the sounds of spoken words.

Since the gaining of speech in all classifications of defects is dependent upon the gaining of the muscular processes which act in sequence upon the air current, let us see how this learning may be gained by those who cannot learn through vision. The remaining sources for learning are adequate to gain speech. We are assuming at this point that the auditory sense is unimpaired. The blind child does not need to *see* in order to receive help through the stimulated pattern. He will learn to associate the sensations which come through *hearing* the word with the *feeling* of the movements which the teacher stimulates.

Careful preparation should be worked out before attempting to stimulate speech sounds for the visually handicapped. Since the blind child cannot see the teacher's hand approaching his mouth, care must be taken not to let the approach come as a surprise or a shock. If the first speech work could be done by the mother, it would be possible to start the stimulations, when her hands are already in contact with the child. For instance, if the face is being washed, mother may say "wash," and then move lips to the mid-line and then into the vowel, as previously directed. Nothing further should be done, no request made for the child to respond at this time, but repetition under similar circumstances will bring the response as the days pass. When putting on the stockings and shoes, mother may say "foot" as she touches the foot. Then some remark like "I will show *your* mouth how to say 'foot,' too." She stops just long enough to move the lower lip against the upper teeth, saying "foot" at the same time, and then proceeds to dress the child. She may set many auditory patterns in the course of the day, letting the child feel the objects named with his hand. In all of this beginning work, there should be nothing attempted except in the child's happiest, quietest moments. The mother takes advantage of the time when the child is holding some object in which he seems interested. Then the mother names it. This kind of work, in which the teaching of the auditory pattern is the objective, could be begun in many cases at about the eighth month. When it can be worked in happily, the child's hand may be brought to the mother's mouth to feel the movements as she speaks the word. Later on, the first two sounds of the word might be stimulated, without yet expecting immediate response. There should be no prolonging of the effort at the time, if there is resistance. The child grows accustomed to these stimulations in time, and will often bring the teacher's hand to his own mouth seeking help, as he feels the need of help in learning to talk.

The senses of smell and taste may also help to build up certain concepts and to enlarge the vocabulary. Simple guessing games may be used. For instance, place an apple, an orange, and a ball before the child. The orange is held to his nose. He smells it, and feels it. It is then placed back among the other objects for him to find again. Mother may let him taste it. He then has the sensations of smell, taste, and feeling of roundness and roughness of surface, associated to form his concept of an orange. The mother gives him the auditory pattern and, when the right moment arrives, moves his mouth through the forms which produce *or* for "orange," or *ap* for "apple." If it were possible for the mother to be ready to make these beginnings toward speech, a good start could be made before the child is taken outside the home for further training. An unhappy condition often exists at the early ages for the visually handicapped. The daily routine occupies the attention of mother or nurse. The mother's anxiety over her child's condition is felt by the child and adds to the difficulty of the situation.

The visually handicapped, like the young hard-of-hearing, find the adjustments to life much more difficult than do so-called normal children. Fear becomes a common reaction to situations which cannot be understood by the handicapped. Disturbing emotions may become dominant during this early period, and thus delay the gaining of speech. Before unhappy emotions gain control, the simplest beginnings toward speech may assist in keeping the child happier and the behavior more normal. Even necessarily slow progress in the beginning shows a cumulative effect with the passage of time. The long-range picture, in which slight begin-

nings, constantly increased, bring a vocabulary in time, may give the
parent courage to attack the problem patiently and hopefully. The early
beginnings allow for time ahead to build up the necessary expressive
movements. Also, the period between the ages of one and three years
seems to be the period when children learn the directed patterns for
words best, as learned through the kinesthetic sense.

From twenty-four months on, more and more words may constantly
be stimulated and learned. If the consonants have found their correct
patterns for simple words, the ear will soon guide the child in gaining
new ones, without direct stimulation. Life would be so much pleasanter,
both for the visually handicapped child and his family, if a speech program could be carried out consistently, in spite of the complexity of daily
living with a child who is visually handicapped. Early home help to the
visually handicapped, and aid to mothers in training these young children,
is being carried out by the Nursery School for the Visually Handicapped
in Los Angeles. Early help for these children is the keynote for greater
accomplishment for all handicapped children, as well as a preventive
measure against greater handicaps.

THE DEAF-BLIND CHILD

It is needless to say that children with the double handicap of blindness and deafness are usually very emotional and unhappy children. The
history of Helen Keller's early life, with all of its frustrations, is generally known. It need not be repeated here. Another description of the
early life and training of a deaf-blind baby is given in a magazine article
entitled "Canada's Mother of Courage."[1] The difficulties connected with
such cases are well shown in this article.

Even in severely handicapped cases, however, there remain some
avenues of learning, as has been demonstrated in Helen Keller's case.
Mental concepts are gained largely through the hands as they reach out
and feel objects around them. Certain qualities of objects are sensed, as
hardness, softness, smoothness, roughness, and weight (heavy or light),
along with elementary number concepts. Since the form of objects is
sensed, reading Braille forms through sense of touch is possible at the
right stage of development. The senses of smell and of taste add in some
instances to the concepts gained by touch. The movements of people, near
enough to them to be felt by the hands, may be sensed and acquired
through the kinesthetic and tactile avenues. In the same way, movements made by another mouth may be felt and learned, as the hand
contacts the mouth of the speaker. The vibrations which come with the
voiced consonants and the vowel sounds are sensed at the same time.
Through these vibrations the deaf-blind are gradually led into the production of voice.

[1] *Coronet*, August 1949.

As the writer watched a demonstration of Helen Keller's work with her teacher, Miss Sullivan, it seemed evident that Helen Keller was finding through the constant contact of her hand with her teacher's muscles of speech, the processes which are used by all mouths in speaking. This learning of muscular movements, with the production of vibrations at the right time, and the sensing of the times when an air current is used without the vibrations, as for the voiceless consonants—these are the factors which count as an inner source for the learning of speech by the deaf-blind. A very limited means of learning, it seems to the normal person. And the upset emotions caused by the hopelessness of the deaf-blind's condition detract constantly from their ability to make best use of their native mentality. The help from within must remain meager and limited, but there is another means to be applied from without, which can greatly strengthen the likelihood of speech to the deaf-blind. This is the directing of speech processes as is done through the moto-kinesthetic method, skillfully applied. This work, tending toward the desired goal, should be begun before the close of the first year, by the child's frequent contact with the mother's face and throat as she talks or sings to her child, in a period preparatory to speech. The hope is that the child will thus begin to sense his means of communication with the outside world. The continuation of the effort is his sensing of movement as he feels his mother's mouth as she says a word. This word should name some object, such as a "shoe," which he is holding. The entire stimulation for "shoe" would include, for the deaf-blind infant of twelve to fifteen months, the feeling of air blown outward as he contacts his mother's mouth and the sensing of the protruding lips, followed by the oncoming vibrations. This experience should be followed by the stimulation to the child's mouth, as the mother moves his mouth through the two-sound sequence. Even if no sound ensues for a period of time, the muscles are going through the beginnings of learning. The habit of moving the muscles for "shoe" is being formed.

Thus the idea, the feel of the mother's mouth as she says a word (thus sensing the sequence of movements), the sensing of vibrations (or the feel of an air current at times without vibrations)—all associated in one learning process—tend toward speech learning. Gradually the names of other objects might be begun in a similar way. The child with a limited mentality, both deaf and blind, may learn to find a limited "way out" through these "lessons," and be happier because of them. Persistence during these first years may keep some children from becoming the unhappy being which Helen Keller is reported to have been before the light of learning began to dawn for her.

One outstanding teacher of the deaf-blind[2] has combined the use of

---

[2] Inis B. Hall, formerly at Perkins Institute and the California State School for the Blind, from which she has recently resigned.

the moto-kinesthetic techniques with her formerly used methods, including the Tadoma[3] technique, for the deaf-blind. The result is highly worthy of the attention of those who are working with this group of children.

Too often these severely handicapped children do not receive help until the best age for starting speech is passed. If mothers of these children could learn to help them at home in infancy, the writer believes that much better results could be achieved. Since speech is primarily achieved through muscular processes, these beginnings, however small, are capable of being built up in a cumulative manner, when correctly learned and associated with ideas.

[3] Tadoma technique is the vibration method.

CHAPTER ELEVEN

THE CEREBRAL PALSIED

In this chapter, the writer is considering the application of the method by which she has seen the speech muscles of some cerebral palsied children gain the correct movements of speech. Specialists in the field have written extensively regarding the causes and conditions found in cerebral palsy, and some of this material is referred to at the end of the book.

Speech, taught to the cerebral palsied through the careful directing of the processes, brings a help greater than that taught through the visual and the auditory senses alone. We have found that this definite way of teaching the speech movements to these children brings results to many of those who are classified among the "cerebral palsied."

It remains for the teachers of these children to learn to direct the movements and processes of speech with *skill* and *accuracy*. The teacher's preparation is of utmost importance. Some of the cerebral palsied are capable of this kind of learning through the kinesthetic sense. Further experimentation will determine which classifications are best adapted to this kind of therapy.

The teacher who is ready to direct the movements of speech should be able to visualize the muscular movements as they act upon the air current through the speaking of a sentence. Close your eyes and try to picture the machinery of the body, in its motor activity, as you say the line "Mary had a little lamb." Can you picture activity in each detail, as the words come out in order? Can you envision it, as the mechanic visualizes the working of his machinery? Can you keep in mind the muscles which are working as the sequence moves on, and which muscle groups are relaxing at any given point? Can you recognize which ones are being stimulated to move next? Are you prepared, as a student, to see this functioning-for-speech, working through certain definite sets of muscles, which may be thought of as apart or isolated from the rest of the muscular movements of the body, like a unit of machinery? It takes time and actual practice to be able to do this.

If you can do this, let us visualize in comparison the movements of a certain cerebral palsied child of three years, with whom the writer worked. She has no speech. Watch while she uses her muscles as she is asked to say words. She wishes to talk, and so starts with an effort which is diffused throughout her body. Sound emerges as a sequence of broken vowels. On this first visit to the clinic the mother says, "Say 'cup,' Mary." Mary tries to say it, but tension mounts with the degree of effort put forth. She does not know how, nor where, to make further effort. Because of her condition, the normal learning of patterns for definite sounds has been thwarted. Following is a recapitulation of the steps which produced the word "cup."

The teacher asked the mother to co-operate with her at this first meeting, to bring about relaxation and a feeling of confidence and calm. A reclining position was used, and the teacher made use of different toys to which attention could be directed objectively. The talk was casual and light. Play was injected sufficiently to make the situation pleasant, but was kept free from excitement, to reduce the extraneous muscle movements. When the moment of understanding had been reached, the teacher said casually something like this, "All of these toys have names, don't they, Mary? This one is a *doll*. This one is a toy *cup*. Your teacher can help your mouth to say 'cup,' just as your mama says it. You do not need to try to say it by yourself. All you need to do is to feel what your teacher does, and make the sounds with her, when she says 'cup.'" The teacher placed her hand outside the throat, under the base of the tongue, making the contact of her hand with the child's throat so gently that no reaction was visible. She then gave the "cu" stimulation (the first two sounds of "cup"), saying "cu" at the same time. The teacher then paused a moment, saying, "Soon *you* will say 'cu,' too. Say it with me, when you feel like trying." Then the teacher stimulated "cu" again, giving the "up-down" stimulation with her hand. Again she said encouragingly, "You will say 'cu' soon." The next repetition did bring it, and the child was overjoyed. In the joy of success, she laughed and the usual form of overflow movements appeared in the habitual manner. The lessons were continued three times a week. New words were stimulated and in a short time the child began to gain words through imitation.

Let us analyze the help which ended in the first spoken word. The child's attempts at speech movements were habitually made outside of those normally required for speech, and she did not know how nor where to start movement for a specific word. If she had known, she might have been unable to direct the correct ones from within, due to her spasticity. When she was assured that she did not need to make effort herself, but sensed her teacher's hand touching the place where the speech pattern should begin, and felt the up-down movements located for her, a tendency toward normal functioning was begun. At the third stimulation she said "cu," because the sequence of movements were directed for her, not brought about by her own effort. She did, however, learn to follow the pattern which was being stimulated.

Fear is expressed that touching the spastic might accentuate his spasticity, or that he might be made "nervous" through this kind of help. There need be no fear of harm to the child, if the teacher will learn the work thoroughly and skillfully. There are many ways of placing the hand in contact with the child's skin. A contact which is not nervously made, and which does not come suddenly, which touches with light pressure on first contact, is reassuring and calming. Then the mouth is led to feel how to move from one sound into the next. The right connections between sounds are made for the child in order to form a word sequence. Extraneous movements are ignored temporarily, concentrating on the feeling of a new set of movements, based upon passive receptivity of mind and body, so far as is possible.

In our experience, the main essential in working on the speech of the cerebral palsied is the step-by-step direction of movements begun early. The exact time or age for beginning depends upon the condition of the child. The small beginning steps as suggested for the young deaf, blind, and deaf-blind children could be begun in many cases between the ages of one and two years. If some adult in care of the child could learn these simple beginnings, the "lessons" could be started at Nature's best age for speech beginnings, and the cumulative effects would bring results in time.

In the selection of words, one should choose those naming objects within the range of the child's interests. After the first word is chosen, another may be selected which starts movement in another set of muscles. If "cup" comes first, possibly "foot" might be next. When the words are directed by the teacher, there seems to be no reason for the preference of one sound over another. If a labial is taught, as "mama" or "baby," the suggestion is to learn this one well, before taking another word beginning with the same set of muscles, such as "papa." It seems best to establish patterns first which are as dissimilar as possible, in order to avoid confusion in learning.

As with other younger children, the cerebral palsied child should not be urged or even asked to say the word at the time of first stimulations, unless he seems ready for such beginnings. He will respond when he himself feels ready to do so, if he is not antagonized when making the effort, or made to feel self-conscious.

The stimulation of real words is much more interesting to any child than single sounds, or babbling sounds, especially to the child who has passed the first two or three years without speech. When teaching words, the object to be named should be present. The first two sounds in immediate blending, as "cu" for "cup," becomes interesting because it sounds like a real word which the child hears others saying. That is what he wants—actual speech.

Fifteen years ago, the writer started speech with a spastic child of five. He was not talking nor walking at the time. Gradually the stimulations for speech were applied, while physiotherapists worked upon his larger muscles. The beginnings of speech came slowly, but were persistently applied for a short period at a time. By his sixth year, he was ready to start reading, and eagerly took the necessary steps in learning.

He has since graduated from high school and, while some spasticity is evident, his life has been removed from the realm of the inadequate and the hopeless.

Another case illustrates the corrective work possible with a spastic adult, which unfortunately had not been attempted in childhood. The corrective work in such cases seems best begun by first working on the most outstanding deviations from the normal movements of speech. In this case it was the movement to produce the *s* sound. She had had some help previously, but always through the auditory and the visual senses, and she had been unable to make a correction through these means. The incorrect movements for *s* started in her tongue, which immediately moved outward toward the right, while her jaw was lowered, which permitted the tongue to come between her teeth. When the tongue was far enough out to permit the elevated back surface to contact the edge of the upper incisors, she blew air outward at the line of contact, as for *th*. This sound of moving air was her substitute for *s*. The appearance of her mouth was most unfortunate, as she was unable to retain the saliva during speech. Therefore, the most obvious need was to work on the *s* first. The teacher explained each step to the patient, in order to enable her to help herself, as she was of average intelligence. She explained, "The jaw should close like this, when *s* comes, instead of opening; you see then, that the tongue should be *inside* the two rows of teeth instead of coming out between them." The teacher raised the jaw to a position in which the lower teeth were close to the upper ones, without actual contact. She then told the patient that when the jaw came to that position, air should move down the central line of the tongue. She then drew the edge of the tongue depressor along this central line. "Now you feel the line down which you will move the air, and then out between your front teeth." The teacher closed the jaw again, sounding the *s* herself, and asked the patient to sound it with her. This time the *s* sound came closer to the hissing *s* than her previously made sound had done. Next, the teacher stimulated words beginning with *s*, such as "see" and "saw," so that the patient might feel the correct moving from the *s* position into the vowels. Before the first lesson was over, she could follow the pattern slowly for "see," "I see," and the like. She could do it because the pattern had been formed for her. She could not follow by watching another mouth, but when the muscles were actually moved for her, she could repeat the same movements again. This patient was able soon to keep her tongue inside her mouth, although she had to control her movements consciously when she felt herself "slipping." These movements could have been taught this spastic person through direct stimulation years previously, with much better speech habits for her use during those years.

Since this volume is a summary of practical helps to the speech-defective, another phase of the teacher's aid to the handicapped may be introduced here, for it is especially applicable to the work with the cerebral palsied. That phase is the attitude of the teacher toward the patient, and her emotional and spiritual qualifications for the work, apart from education and training.

There should be a deep-seated interest in the handicapped as such. There should be sufficient insight into the condition to permit the teacher to see the real child apart from his handicap, and to enable her to work in a spirit of patient gladness, in order to bring about the results required. More than that, there should be within these teachers a love for the ones with whom they are working—an affection which shines in the face and eyes, and speaks through the sound of the voice, acting as an inspiration to those who are facing some of life's most difficult situations through no fault of their own. Only those who are strong in spirit, peaceful in soul, and filled with the desire to give, and who keep these qualities consistently alive, should work with the handicapped.

The writer has seen teachers of the handicapped who answer to this description. She has seen them thrill to the slightest gains on the part of their pupils. She has watched them, as they do their tasks with unwearied patience. From them she has learned the meaning of what a teacher of the handicapped should be!

CHAPTER TWELVE

THE APHASIC

Let us now consider how the moto-kinesthetic method may be applied toward restoring the speech of the aphasic, i.e., those who are ready physically to begin speech work. There will be no attempt made at the classification of the conditions which cause aphasia. References are given at the close of the volume to enable the student to understand the whole picture from the standpoint of medical science. The writer's reason for writing this chapter is that she has seen the definite stimulations of movements work successfully to bring about the recall of words, where recall had failed without it. Here is an example: A certain business man had suffered a brain hemorrhage. He was able to return to work eventually, but had not recovered his speech. At the clinic where they attempted to bring about the recall of words, an appeal was made to various senses. They brought an orange before him. "What do we do before we can eat it? *You* get it ready to eat." The man began to peel it, as he had done formerly. The clinician said, "We peel the ———," hoping the word "orange" might emerge at this point, but it did not come. "Smell it." The man smelled it. The clinician said "The ——— smells good. *What* smells good?" The man tried to think of the name, but the name did not come.

Next, they used a pin, asking him what he could do with it. He showed them. They stuck him with it slightly, but no word came. There is one more thing which they could have done, which might have helped. We shall see, later on, what this other possibility is.

At the outset, the writer wishes to differentiate between children who have always been speechless and adults who had previously learned speech and had talked in the usual manner, until a brain accident or lesion had caused loss of speech. Unless the child is in a similar condition, his speechlessness may have come through failure to acquire the necessary learning process. (See the chapter on "Delayed Speech.") Muscles cannot function for speech without undergoing a practice period, such as any normal young child experiences. The adult who loses speech, after having used it normally, seems to be in a different category from the child who is speechless and whose muscles have never passed through the definite speech learning processes. In the case of the adult, the neuro-muscular learning has been there, but the connection has been broken between ideas and the definite expressive activity of muscles used previously to express those ideas. In such cases the moto-kinesthetic training has been found to be especially valuable. No individual, without knowledge of the speech processes, has any good understanding of how his muscles functioned before he lost his speech. The trained teacher, who helps the aphasic to *feel* former patterns—to experience the actual process again—has the best means at his command for restoring speech. All other senses should be used to induce a memory of the name of the object, as was done in the clinic previously mentioned; but when the subject *feels* his mouth functioning as it formerly did, the memory of this formerly learned activity is often revived, and he may be able to speak the word alone, after a few applications of the stimulation.

One patient, who suffered a cerebral hemorrhage, and whose speech was affected, pointed to a glass of water. This happened in the afternoon of the day in which the stroke occurred. The mouth was moved to the mid-line, in the rounded *oo* position, then quickly brought downward as in *wa.* The patient responded and got *wa.* By the third day, he was saying *wa* spontaneously when he wanted water. The patient was constantly assured that his speech would return, and whenever an opportune time arose, other words were casually stimulated. By the end of the first month, enough words were restored with which to express many daily needs. As his general physical condition improved, his mental condition cleared considerably, and by the end of three months after his stroke his speech became sufficient to make his needs well understood. It was practically normal by the close of the sixth month.

Two women aphasics, one forty-six, the other sixty years of age, both responded to the stimulations for the sentence, "I want a book." Both were able to say the sentence at the close of the first lesson. The younger woman retained the movements and repeated the sentence to her husband after she returned home, omitting only the final sound in "want." The older woman retained "book." The speech of the younger woman returned sufficiently to express her thoughts in simple sentences, as "Put the cat out" and "Dinner is ready."

The older woman had had a brain accident five years before the help on speech began. After the accident she had used the syllable *ba, ba* repeatedly in her effort to talk. This habit continued after she had learned a few single words. She would often start with a word, and then continue with *ba, ba, ba,* until she had completed the usual length of a sentence, with the syllables, as "Go-ba, ba, ba, ba, ba." This older woman did not recover the use of whole sentences, but she used many single words. In her case, we felt that the work on speech, with the consequent use of some single words, was a morale builder. She was happier with the recovery of even a few usable words, and often showed, with pleasure and satisfaction, the meaning back of the word used. Another woman, who experienced speechlessness for a month, following a slight stroke, described her experience (after regaining her speech) as the most baffling, hopeless experience of her lifetime. She felt terrified, upon suddenly being unable to talk to her family. She felt imprisoned within herself.

The writer's experience with the aphasic adult would indicate that there should be more experimentation to co-ordinate motor stimulations for the recall of the definite movements with the effort toward recall through the other senses. The encouragement which comes to the patient when he hears a real word, issuing again from his own mouth, is tremendous, and is a decided help to the patient emotionally.

There are two points which seem to us important. One is to start giving some help to the patient as soon as he attempts speech after his accident or stroke, and when he shows concern because he is unable to talk. At the same time he should be assured, if his physical condition permits, that he will talk again, and that he may have hope in the meantime. The second point is that the definite stimulation of movements, as described in this book, should be applied one step at a time, because it is a surer way of recalling the word. The idea which the word expresses, the instructor's auditory pattern, and the clearly presented concept of the use and place of the object named should accompany the stimulation of the muscular pattern for saying the word.

CHAPTER THIRTEEN

THE ADAPTATION
OF THE MOTO-KINESTHETIC METHOD TO THE
DEVELOPMENT OF INFANT SPEECH

For many years the writer experimented in directing the speech move-ments of children of various ages and of adults who were having speech difficulty. The only age level left without such experimentation was the younger level—that of the preschool child and, younger still, the infant beginning speech. The normal infant of eight or nine months has a men-tal alertness and awareness of his environment far beyond his power of expression. Up to this point in his development, the time has been passed in attaining physical growth and in the maturation of certain processes, as a foundation for further development.

There is a great difference in the ages at which children start to talk. Some are saying many words at eight months; others have said none at all. But somewhere between eight months and one year, the time arrives when the average infant is making a very apparent effort to express his developing thoughts and feelings. He gives evidence of having ideas to express, but he has not yet acquired the use of the tools for expression which must come through a gradual learning process. This learning proc-ess involves the gaining of one step at a time. It cannot be forced, but it can be aided. The nervous system must not be overtaxed, as it re-quires time to build up the necessary neuromuscular controls. The aid comes in helping to bring about the correct use of muscles, as the step-by-step process is gained. The child has babbled (if he is a normal infant), and his muscles have moved through some (if not all) of the sequences which are used later in speech, as "ba ba," "da da," etc. But when he attempts to follow certain sound patterns, or the names of objects as spoken to him, he is not always able to bridge the gap between his babbling and the sequence of sounds used in saying words correctly.

Even if his babbling has included all of the sounds of speech, never-theless he has not babbled in the exact order of sounds which now con-front him. He mistakes one sound for another, bearing some likeness to it; he may call "cup," "tup." It is just at this period, when the infant is trying to find the way into speech, that a little help through directing the muscles, makes the task much lighter and at the same time permits him to enjoy this means of self-expression in a more satisfactory way, because he finds that he is being understood through it.

When considering the means of adapting the moto-kinesthetic method to infant speech, it is important to know just what the writer means. Let it be said at the outset that the basis for the use of these techniques is the same basis as that which all the centuries have employed, where loving mothers have had the time and opportunity to help their children develop speech. The auditory pattern for words has always been a part of the procedure. The visual stimulation has been used with the auditory to show the child how the adult forms his words. With this background as the foundation, let us insert a little more help through the kinesthetic sense in the gaining of speech.

In order to see the application more clearly, let us imagine a home situation which will carry out the writer's ideas in speech training for the infant, as based upon her own experience. In this home which we are about to observe, the mother and father are happily mated—thus creating the kind of environment in which a child develops best; and there is a small son seven months of age. The parents are looking ahead, planning on steps which are to be taken for both physical and mental growth. The mother has learned the most important stimulations of the moto-kines-thetic method, because she wants to give the child the benefit of all possible help when the right time arrives. However, there is much to do in prepa-ration for speech learning before the moto-kinesthetic work begins. So let us look in on her as she lives with her child from day to day. She talks to him whenever she is near him, as he sits in his little crib or pen, with playthings scattered around. Her voice is sweet and loving, but she uses no baby talk. She talks spontaneously about the things around them. There are toys which run on wheels; she makes them run and says, "go." She names objects, using just one word at a time. She does not attempt to force his attention to her activities, simply letting him absorb what he will in his own way.

The weeks go by, and the child reaches eight months of age. The two "hold conversations" together. The mother accepts his babbling as real talk and answers him, with a fine way of appealing to his budding sense of humor. Little changes in facial expression or movements of arms or body in some unusual way appeal to him as funny, and they laugh to-gether a great deal. When she has the thought of his learning in mind, she says only one word at a time, and holds the object which she names; but she does not ask him to say it. She is watching now for that time to come when she may help him more definitely. The exact age for this step cannot be stated, but somewhere between eight months and one year, if it has not already come, most children are ready for a beginning of this kind of training. The mother watches for that right moment when the child is pouring out his babble to her and is all but saying real words, in order to start her moto-kinesthetic help. She has named the toys many times, the foot, the hand, and the nose. Perhaps she does this again, and then starts the stimulation process by touching his foot, and repeating the name, to give a clear auditory pattern. If she has held his interest up to this point, she moves her own lower lip against her upper teeth, where he can see the process, and says "foot" again. Then she moves *his* lip toward the upper gums or teeth. She does it gently and carefully only once this time, and goes on talking casually as before. She does not expect the child to say "foot" at this point, but the learning is beginning to take root. The feeling of his mother's hand on his lip, thus locating his beginning activity for "foot," witn the feeling of the upward movement, remains. She is not concerned as to when the response is to appear; it will come in time. She wants it to come when he is ready to give it. She may hear it for the first time as he is talking to himself in his crib. She is very careful not to attempt stimulations except at chosen moments. She has learned, in fact, to know when he is apt to be most interested, and takes advantage of his more co-operative moments in which to make these beginnings toward speech learning.

She may not be able to move the mouth for all of *foo* at first. The first effort may only move the lip upward, but he is used to having her do things for him—wash his face, feed him, etc.—and at some convenient, right moment she manages to stimulate both processes, and says "foo" at the same time. Very soon she may see the lower lip begin to move as she says the word "foot," and by repetition of the stimulations, she may be confident that the use of the upward movement of the lower lip will start the *f* words, ensuring "foot" instead of "toot" or "soot." She knows now that one beginning has been made toward a permanent habit, never to be changed. Every repetition strengthens its use into permanent habit formation.

Next, the mother-teacher chooses to start a word which involves action at the back of the mouth, and decides to stimulate the word "cup" as a beginning. She keeps the child's little cup on hand, and names it frequently, pretends to drink milk from it, as if with great enjoyment, and the baby laughs with mother over the pretense, which may appeal to him as funny at this stage of his development.

When the head position and general attitude seem just right, she lowers his jaw, places thumb and forefinger under the back of his tongue outside, and gently and carefully moves them up, then down, and says "cup," but she does not emit the last sound too forcefully, as the final sound is not to be stimulated until "cu" is fused and comes readily into use. She may or may not have to stimulate this *k* sound several times in the next weeks before it comes easily, if the child has not made it before. It should be done only once at each effort, followed by something over which there can be pleasure, in order to build up a happy feeling in the effort, and a desire to have it repeated.

The weeks pass, and the baby is learning to creep. Mother is careful not to let her thought of speech training interfere with his new joy in using his larger muscles, but the time comes when he needs to be fed, and moving about is stopped for the time being. Mother uses the opportunity to talk about "milk in the cup," as she pours milk from the bottle. It makes a gurgling sound, and mother imitates it, and laughs over it.

She says "milk." And when the right moment comes she closes his lower lip against the upper, touches the bridge of his nose, and says "milk." She will not let any help on speech interfere with his moments of hunger. Such help must come after hunger is satisfied, at least partially. The baby has doubtlessly made the sound of *m* many times in his babbling, and now the stimulation for "mi" is a step which associates the former learning with the milk which he is drinking. From the many forms of babbling, which he has formerly used, this particular form is now isolated to stand for "milk."

Next, she takes a tongue end beginning, such as "to" for "top." There is much room for fun, in seeing the top spin. She constantly directs the attention to something interesting outside himself, which through the effect of smiles and laughter leaves no trace of self-consciousness as the child learns. She does not teach two tongue-end sounds in succession. "To" should be learned as standing for "top" before another tongue-end sound is stimulated. She has planned to stimulate "shoe" next, as it is often used in daily life, and it can be done so satisfactorily in dressing. She always stimulates the names of objects close at hand. Perhaps "pan" next, then "dog," if there is a dog in the family. She waits until "pa" for "pan" comes easily before stimulating "ball," so as not to confuse the processes which are made in the same part of the mouth. Then "go" may follow. They have often told the car to "go." The father "goes" each morning.

It is now the eleventh or twelfth month. The mother tries to stimulate new forms before the baby has a chance to make them by himself, so that the learning may be done correctly. He is learning fast now, and he does not need the physical stimulations for many new words at this point, as he has already associated sound beginnings with the correct process previously. He says "car" and "come." She sets the pattern for *w* so that she may teach "want," to enable him to ask for what he wants. Then "I want." From twelve to fifteen months, new words and parts of sentences are added constantly, through imitation largely, as he listens to spoken words. Mother is on guard, and when she hears an incorrect form, she waits until the right time comes and stimulates the correction.

From the preceding description, you have a partial picture, at least, of the writer's concept of teaching speech correctly when it is first learned. The ease with which the infant learns through the feel of the stimulations is amazing. There is no previous pattern to obstruct the learning.

Next, the writer will present a few factual experiences in her own work on infant speech:

Case 1.—The writer spent an afternoon with Jean. The child was wearing a new pair of shoes, which were pretty, in a bright color, and she toddled over and said, "Soot, soot," looking at her feet to call attention to her new shoes. The writer admired the new shoes and pretended, to make Jean laugh, that she wanted to put them on her own feet. Then the teacher said, "Foot,

foot," moving her own lip against her upper teeth. Jean looked curiously at the writer's mouth, and her first reaction was to turn her back and toddle back to her play pen. She picked up a toy, but couldn't forget her late experience. She pulled herself up, came back, and stood closer, and held her head tipped up, to get the writer to help her to say "foot." Jean held still and permitted her lip to be moved up. Then she blew the air between the lip and the upper teeth for the "f," which was immediately turned into "foo" by the writer. For the next hour Jean vacillated between playing and coming for help to say *foo* again. By the close of the afternoon, she could say it by herself.

The writer spent occasional afternoons with Jean during the next year, amounting altogether to about a dozen times. The child was most happy to have help with her speech, and the writer would stimulate corrections if she had learned some new word incorrectly. Jean's mother checked, and found that no mistake lasted longer than two weeks. By two years, all corrections were over. As her mother read nursery rhymes to her, the auditory pattern was all that was needed, and she was able to repeat correctly the lines which her mother read.

Case 2.—Patty was between seven and eight months when the following incident occurred. Conditions had been such that the writer had seen her practically every week since birth, so they were very well acquainted by the time of the speech-acquiring stage. There was no reason to think that Patty would not talk, since she was an alert normal baby who had babbled normally, but the mother was willing for her baby to have any constructive help which might be given her. At the time of this story, Patty had not previously attempted any response to the auditory pattern for "foot." Since the stimulation is to the lower lip, which is easily accessible to the teacher, this word is a good one with which to start the stimulations. A gradual conditioning process is also a part of the work, and the first stimulations must be done in as short a length of time as possible, but without any appearance of hurry, or sudden action. The hand should come to the lip with an assuring, easy movement, and make itself felt on the lip, with a slight upward movement. That is all that is necessary in the first attempt. If it becomes a lingering process, the infant, not yet conditioned, will turn away from it. By the time the stimulation just mentioned has been given, the hand is withdrawn. The writer felt that the time had come for Patty to be ready for the beginning attempt. She wanted to bring about a situation in which the attention might be kept on something objective, so she lifted Patty up on her left arm, keeping her right hand free to be used if the right moment came. They went about the room looking at the pictures and toys. Here was a doll, and here a doll's "foot." The writer said "foot." Patty watched her say it, and listened. Then the right opportunity was at hand. The *foo* sound was stimulated, for she showed no signs of objection, and the two went on looking at the toys. The writer made the doll walk with her "foot," and both laughed over the absurd performance. Patty showed no sign of response that day. The next day, they started the same procedure to see if it would be conducive to the recall of the stimulation of the day before. The child did not wait for a repetition of the stimulation, but turned to the writer and blurted out *foo* in a rather loud voice for one so small, as much as to say, "I got ahead of you that time! You didn't have to show me but once!"

Another illustrative incident comes from the work with Patty. She was beginning to walk at this time, and used many words, partly gained through imitation, since she heard speech, but the unused sounds were also being stimulated one by one in the short lessons. The *k* sound in "cup" had not found its way into use yet, so the teacher watched for the right opportunity to stimulate it. Patty had her own little drinking cup in her hand, pretending to drink from it. The teacher slipped her hand under the raised chin, and gave the stimulation, saying "cup." Patty responded immediately, walking off into the room, experimenting with this new feeling, and repeating the first two sounds. However, that one stimulation did the trick. That noon the nurse poured milk into Patty's cup, and Patty responded immediately with "cu." The nurse was so delighted that she rushed to find Patty's mother, exclaiming "Patty just said 'cup.' Patty just said 'cup'!"

Children respond differently, both in interest shown and in the length of time before the actual response occurs, as the next incident shows.

Case 3.—The infant in this story, ten months of age, had an older brother who had not developed speech. Doubtless this factor had influenced the younger child, for he rarely made any sounds. While the writer was working with the other brother, the mother brought the infant with her. This gave the writer another opportunity for experimentation. The first effort was to find the way by which the baby could be amused. He very seldom cried but he was too serious, although a beautiful, intelligent-looking child. We went through the play procedures for two weeks, named objects, and finally the writer stimulated the first word, "foot." It was stimulated for a month before the word was spoken. Then, at long last, after waking from a midmorning nap, as the writer entered the room, the baby turned to her and said "foo," his first word. The writer was not able to continue work with this child, so cannot report any further on this case.

Case 4. The twins.—They were nine months of age when the writer first saw them, as the mother was wheeling them past the writer's home. The history of twins whom she had previously known was recalled by her—children of five or six without intelligible speech, although they seemed to understand each other. With this thought in mind, the writer approached the mother for the purpose of another experiment. As they lived close by, the writer at first saw these twins twice a week. Later on, the periods were farther apart. In the beginning, the mother would spread out a large blanket on the living room floor and place the babies on it, spreading out their toys around them. The writer worked into the play gradually, leaving them to their own initiative, until she had a fairly good idea of their development and effort toward speech. They constantly babbled sounds, but said no words. The procedure of leading them into speech need not be repeated, since it conformed to the previous illustrations given in this chapter. But by the end of a year's work both twins were talking plainly. Here is a conversation recorded at the close of their twenty-second month. First twin: "Here is a box. I put my toys in it." Second twin: "No, I want that box. You can't have it. Give it to me."

Case 5. A boy of twenty-two months.—No speech; birth and development normal otherwise. He played hard, but had no interest in learning speech. The pediatrician advised speech training. The usual procedure was followed by which the child was led into play, and then the stimulations of the moto-kinesthetic method began. His mother stood at the head of the speech table as the word "Mama" was stimulated. He had not even said that beginning word up to this time. It was a thrilling moment for her, when she heard him say it as a result of the stimulations. He recognized his success and repeated the word happily several times, voluntarily.

The value of speech was well illustrated in his case a year later, when the mother was away for a few days. The first night, the father put the child to bed, and he went without objection. The next night at bedtime, he objected, cried, and seemed fearful to go to his room. The father held him, and tried to calm his fears, but still he was unwilling to go to bed. Then as the father questioned him as to why he did not want to go, he said, "I don't like that man that crawled in the window, and came and looked at me." Then the father examined the window, and found that both window and screen had been opened, although he had not been aware of it previously.

Case 6.—Some years ago the writer joined a research class at a university where each member undertook a research problem in which he was interested. The writer chose to record the speech development of five children with defective speech and also of one infant ten months of age. The moto-kinesthetic method of speech correction was to be used, as applied to each case in hand. The case described here is one which did not react quickly to training in the beginning. The mouth had assumed and kept the sucking position too long, with the tongue slightly outside. This case is offered to show the difference in the way in which young children are able to respond to speech learning.

Jim had a severe case of whooping cough at the age of three months, which may have accentuated a forward movement of the tongue. The student will note that while Jim had turned away from speech learning at ten months, he showed a remarkable effort to acquire his words correctly after he became interested. For brevity's sake, only excerpts from records at various dates are given here. The teacher is designated as T. and the infant as Jim.

Date, November 4.

T. first contacts Jim at ten months. Jim's muscles all move clumsily, and his speech muscles are no exception. He is still creeping at ten months. He is not interested in speech, but prefers much activity of other kinds. Jim's mouth is open most of the time, tongue slightly forward, lips rounded as for sucking. Once he stopped in this first contact and looked at T., as if talking about the ball, threw arms upward, intoned sounds about the length of a sentence, ending with a questioning "huh?" They play ball together. T. presses her own lips together and says "ball," as she returns the ball. She gives no indication that he is to follow. No effort toward response, visible or audible.

Date, November 18.

Similar play procedure. T. presses Jim's lips together, and then brings the jaw downward. She repeats six times at different intervals. Goes on playing with ball. All very casual. Jim said "ba" once, leaving off the *l*, and then threw the ball.

Date, November 22.

T. and Jim each take tongue depressors. T. puts hers in her mouth, holding the end down and says "catch." Then she throws the ball up and says "catch" as it comes down. Jim, interested, tries to do the same. T. takes his tongue depressor. He opens his mouth. Jim responds with "ca" twice as T. stimulates it. They throw the ball back and forth, T. saying "catch ball."

Date, November 28.

Same procedure.

Date, December 3.

T. stimulated "ca" twice for "catch." Stimulation for beginning of "pin," as Jim holds a big safety pin. Jim puts tongue depressor in own mouth. T. turned it into "ca" with the tongue depressor.

Date, December 10.

On arrival, the nurse told T. that Jim had just said "bye-bye" for first time. In this lesson, Jim said "ba" five times for "ball," "ca" for "catch" three times. T. started auditory pattern on "ball up," "ball down," using the ball at the same time.

Date, December 12.

Spontaneous words: Jim said "bye-bye," "ba" four times ("ball"), "ca" once ("catch"). Began stimulating for "foot." Jim said "ba down" once, after T. had said it.

Date, December 17.

Jim said "ba, ca, up." Further work for "foot." Jim makes the blowing sound as T. holds lip. Tries to get it, but cannot get lip up alone. The shape of the rounded mouth interferes.

Date, January 13, the following year.

Jim took his first steps today, at 11 months of age. T. stimulated "walk." Jim said "wa" afterward.

Date, January 16.

T. started work for *l*, by inserting tongue depressor. Jim cannot lift his tongue by himself, but he took the tongue depressor and held the end of his tongue down for "ca" ("catch").

Date, January 19.

Jim is walking more now. More interested in that than speech. T. must watch for the right moment to help with speech. Stimulated "my." Jim responded with "my" alone.

Date, February 3.

Jim talked in the form of sentences, using "my," "da," "ca," "ba," in quick succession, as if in real speech. Started the pattern for *s*. Jim said "ba" (*a* as in "at") three times, when T. said "bear." He said "ca ba" when playing ball ("catch ball").

Date, February 24.

T. stimulated word "book." Jim got all of that word. Also worked on the *t* sound, for "to-too"—sound of engine. Jim rolled car, saying "too-too." As we rolled the ball, Jim said "ro" five times in response to "roll ball."

Date, March 2.

Today T. invited two other small boys to be with them at Jim's lesson, as these boys were already conditioned to longer lessons than Jim. They had their lesson and Jim tried to do as they did. He wanted a tongue depressor, put it in his mouth, pushed the back of his tongue up, and said "cock" for "clock." All three boys got "shoe" when stimulated to say it.

Date, March 10.

Jim teething. Not much response. We played quietly. Jim said "ro ba" alone ("roll ball").

Date, April 7–10.

Jim is becoming conditioned to longer periods of training. He worked happily for one minute at a time today. Says "fat, mat, cat, pat, hat, rat, come," as T. changes stimulations. Each day, repetition of *l* and *s* stimulations. Lower lip not ready for automatic action for *f*. (The sucking position still in evidence but giving way to new controls used in speech lessons.)

Date, April 20–24.

Spontaneous words spoken: "ball, see daddy, mama, peek-a-boo, doll, eat, up, down, paper, basket." Whole pattern for *s* done twice in one-and-a-half minutes. *l* pattern stimulated three times.

Date, April 24.

Best spontaneous words: "car go, baby down." T. lifted Jim's tongue three times for "light." (Jim's tongue had learned to move, forward and back, out and then in, through the opening formed by the sucking formation. Much help seems needed to establish changes).

Date, April 28.

Spontaneous words: "wet-oh, wet" (he fell in the water), "daw" for "doll" (no *l*), "foot," "mamma," "ba" (no *l*). Pattern set of "I go home to mamma." Said correctly as T. directed "go."

Date, May 3.

Patterns for words beginning with *s, l, f*. Jim's tongue, being in the *e* position a great deal, says "yight" for "light." Set pattern for "bath." Pattern sentences: "I sit down," "I want bread," "I get up." Jim is making a very apparent effort to say "light" by himself. He stops under the light, looks at it, and says painstakingly, "e-yight." T. stops and lifts tongue slightly at the tip. Jim says "light" with this help, and goes to play contented.

Date, May 30.

Jim says "foot" alone, with correct movement for *f* for the first time.

Date, June 10.

Jim tried "light" again, said "yight," then grasped T.'s hand and put it to his mouth to help him say it. T. helped him three times. Spontaneous words: "See John fall down," "Shut door," "Oh, boy," "Open door," "See Bobby" (poor *s*), "Want bread," "Dog bark," "New tie."

Date, June 13.

Tongue end lifts a little more for the *l*. The *s* sound is improving. The tongue does not come quite as far out as formerly. Jim often comes with a book and wants to talk about the pictures.

On April 7, Jim said nine different words spontaneously. By April 20, twenty-one words. By June 13, at one-and-a-half years, he had used fifty-two words. In lessons, he can repeat seventy-four words (with help on *s* and *l*).

Date, June 22.

Jim says "light" alone correctly for the first time. As T. is with Jim, she says simple sentences to express the activity of the moment: "I go to bed," "I catch a ball," etc. Special attention to the ending of words is given now. T. asked Jim to say "lamp." He reached for her hand, and said "tick" ("stick") and pushed it up to his mouth.

Jim walked down fourteen steps today, without holding on with his hands. Very much interested in getting speech lessons now. T. helps him only when he comes for it. Jim found T. standing, giving a lesson. He pushed a chair to her and said, "Sit down."

Date, July 13.

Jim nineteen months old. Spontaneous words since June 13, one hundred twenty-seven. Answer to question, "Where is your bottle?" Jim says, "Bottle fall down."

Date, September 1.

(No lessons in August.) Jim says "yight," "baf" (for "bath"). T. corrects again. Stimulates "bath" three times. Then Jim says it correctly again.

Date, September 16.

Three stimulations daily for "bath," "light," and "see."

Date, September 23.

Daily repetition of stimulations for *s*, *l*, and *th*. Many more spontaneous sentences of which these are the best: "I want my paper," "Tommy fall down," "I want milk," "So good" (while eating a tomato).

Date, October 7–9.

Jim worked happily for two minutes on sounds which he had used incorrectly when talking.

Date, October 13.

Jim has now said 270 different words in his lessons, and can repeat them after T. She corrects them if mistakes occur.

Date, October 31.

T. continues with 'stimulation for words containing *l*, *th*, and *s*. Best sentences at close of October: "Where's the fork?" "Can't find it," "Cat down there," "All gone." Jim looked at a page of cow pictures and said, "No doggie there, no kitty there. Only just cows."

Summary of Jim's speech work:

At close of one year of work, at 22 months, Jim has said 321 different words spontaneously. He needs more help for words containing the *sh*, *ch*, and *s* sounds. The mouth habits of a year ago are being overcome, and good progress in that direction has been made. Jim starts his sentences with "I" now, if indicating himself.

Jim's rate of increase in spoken words:

To November 4—2 words.
November 4 to next April 7—9 words.
April 21 (at 16 months)—21 spontaneous words; 17 more spoken through stimulation in lessons.
June 13 (at 18 months)—52 words used spontaneously.
July 13 (at 19 months)—112 words used spontaneously.
October 13 (at 22 months)—270 words used spontaneously.
November 4 (at 23 months 22 days)—321 words used spontaneously.

CONCLUSIONS DRAWN BY WRITER
AS A RESULT OF HER WORK ON INFANT SPEECH

1. Use the usual way of developing infant speech, but add a careful adaptation of the moto-kinesthetic method. Through this combination of methods the infant may learn speech more easily, with less frustrations.

2. Prevention of much speech difficulty could be brought about by the infant's learning speech correctly, when he begins to use words.

3. Each process learned correctly builds up habits which need no change, making for stability and permanence in functioning. Each use, therefore, makes the muscular habits stronger from infancy on. The brain is free to think and to express. The tools for its permanent use have been gained. The usual effort toward correction is minimized. This is bound to be a great aid in personality development, as compared with that of the child who plods on, without correct speech habits, and is given no help in acquiring the correct patterns or engrams of speech.

CHAPTER FOURTEEN

STUTTERING

At the beginning of this chapter, the writer wishes to express her deep appreciation of the work on stuttering which has been accomplished by others in recent years. The constructive advice for treatment of the young child, as well as the training of the parents to bring about co-operative help, has been a big step forward. The treatise, *Stuttering*,[1] prepared for the American Speech and Hearing Association, furnishes a sound basis for both parent and teacher who look for reliable help along this line. If this treatise could be followed invariably in its spirit and practical suggestions for daily living with children, there would be fewer primary stutterers who would go into the secondary stage. However, from the writer's viewpoint and experience, there is another factor which is a part of the onset of stuttering, which must be taken into account and dealt with, in order to come closer to the total concept—a therapy which is capable of possible adjustment to that concept.

Since it is accepted in scientific research that all factual data relating to an area of study are vital to the total effort, the writer has felt for years the necessity for bringing certain indisputable facts connected with her own experience to the closer attention of those who are working to solve the problem of stuttering. In order to do this, it seems necessary to state the steps in the writer's own experience, which led to her interpretation of some of the phenomena seen in stuttering.

Through the constant effort of years in which the control of speech, moment by moment, was the paramount goal, underlying her life and work as a teacher, the writer gained her motivation for her later work on speech problems. She felt that there should be some way to utilize her own personal experience so as to help others with speech difficulty. Therefore, with the utmost humility but with a firm belief in the reliability of the work which has developed out of this experience, she is writing in order to leave a record of what she has felt, experienced, and interpreted in others. The facts which the writer presents as having a definite relationship to the problem of stuttering were not a part of the personal problem as she began her study of speech. However, it seems necessary to give the actual experience preceding these facts, in order to have a clear picture of the events as they occurred, and which led finally to the definite experience which she wishes to present in writing this chapter.

From an early age, the writer remembers a constant effort to talk plainly, although she was not aware of how to bring this about. From time to time, a brother or sister would speak of her talking "one-sided,"

---

[1] By Charles Van Riper, under the editorship of Wendell Johnson.

but the sound of speech was understandable judging by the fact that she was not asked to repeat what she had said. By the age of fifteen years, she had become aware of the fact that her speech movements varied from those of others. Since her mouth muscles were uncomfortable in speech, she determined to study the speech problem involved. She began by watching the speech movements of other people as they talked. She found, in the course of some three years, certain characteristics of normal speech, and contrasted them with her own speech movements.

1. As people talk, the jaw moves in a perpendicular line, straight up and down. *Her* jaw constantly moved to the right, and back to the center.

2. The usual tongue action is to the mid-line of the dental ridge, as the sounds of *t*, *d*, *n*, and *l* occur in speech. *Her* tongue rose in the center to make these sounds, not using the tongue tip, which had to be free to turn to the right for *s* and *z*.

3. When *s* and *z* sounds came, the average person closes the jaws sufficiently to hide the tongue action, which appeared to take place at the middle of the mouth. *Her* lower jaw could not reach the upper except at one point, where an outer cusp of a molar extended upward, separating the jaws. Her tongue tip appeared at the right, contacting the inner edge of the upper right lip as *s* and *z* were made. Thus the tongue end came through the opening between the jaws, close to the cusp in question, extending far enough to contact the inner edge of the upper lip.

4. The lips in most persons seemed to move equally from the mid-line to corners and back, making the same appearance on each side of the mid-line. *Her* lower lip moved as a unit toward the right corner.

5. Most mouths move easily and comfortably in speech. *She* was constantly aware of a certain discomfort, which she came to believe must be due to the differences which she had found in her own mouth habits, and those of other speakers. The irregular tooth which kept her jaws apart seemed to be at the base of the difficulty. While reading or working, she found herself often pushing her jaw outward and to the right, to avoid this one-point contact.

Facts which seemed pertinent to the study came very slowly at first. Gradually, as she watched people talk, she isolated certain movements and forms which invariably took place in the production of a given sound. Three years, between the fifteenth and eighteenth years of age, were spent in close observation and effort, to reproduce the sounds as others made them, so far as she was able to discover the pertinent facts. At eighteen the irregular tooth became abscessed, from constant grinding, and was extracted. This allowed the speech practice to become more normal, since the lower jaw could then come closer to the upper, without the wide opening between them. However, it was through constant effort and manual manipulation that the tongue, jaw, and lips could be made to co-

ordinate their activity and assume the correct functioning, even temporarily in practice.

By the age of twenty-two the writer could talk using two distinctly
different sequences of movements, for any given sentence. The more
newly acquired use of muscles had been used in practice only when alone.
In daily speech with others, she used her first learned movements, since
she did not feel sure of the strength of the new habits which she had been
acquiring. While wondering about her readiness to use her new learning
in daily speech, a wisdom tooth began to emerge, causing swelling and a
set immovable condition of the jaws which lasted for a period of two
weeks. Since her jaw could not move to the right during this period, the
writer followed this incident with the beginning of the complete change
to the later learned speech movements. This involved much change of
habit.

1. A change from a one-sided movement of the jaw to an attempted
straight up-down action.

2. A change in all the activity of the tongue, bringing it back to the
middle of the mouth instead of allowing the movement to the right, and
thus letting the tip relate itself to the mid-line of the dental ridge for
s and *z*.

3. A retraining in the use of the lower lip (a difficult task). The
movement of the whole lip to the right had to be replaced by a bilateral
use of its two parts, in which both move symmetrically, in unison, when
gliding either toward the mid-line or away from it.

4. Every sound of speech required one or more changes in muscular
movements, in order to function according to the normal pattern.

These changes had been practiced in their normal relationship to other
sounds in words and sentences. By the age of twenty-two, when practicing alone, the writer had no difficulty in reading, or in speaking sentences, following out the necessary changes in jaw, tongue, and lips. She
took it for granted that all her speech difficulty would soon be at an end,
but to her complete amazement, the real trouble had just begun. The constant adherence to the new patterns of functioning brought something
entirely new into the experience. Since she had mentally discarded the
first learning, and had learned and substituted another to replace it, she
had expected the corrected forms to take their places comfortably. She
was amazed and terrified at what she began to experience. The former
patterns of movement began to appear in consciousness just where they
had occurred previously and forcefully persisted in their attempt to
function as formerly. The tendency to press the jaw and tongue to the
right was particularly strong, making control of the movements difficult.
The next three years required constant attention to speech in which the
clarification of the desired forms was needed several times daily in order
to keep them segregated mentally from the first learned sequences. The

desired movements were aided manually each time, since the aid brought the *feeling* of correct movements in the parts concerned, while associating them with the visual and auditory patterns.

It was necessary to keep consistently at this renewal of the correct functioning. If a few days passed without practice, the first learning would be felt more strongly again, tending to confuse the conscious mental direction of the desired movements. Deliberate help of the conscious mind was an undercurrent in daily speech; thus the mental effort was doubled. It was necessary during these years to think not only of what to say, but consciously to aid in saying it. More concentrated attention was required when tired or ill. A plan had to be made by which, at such times, more rest from speech could be obtained, and it had to be limited to only that which was absolutely essential. The involuntary habits which had come with the earlier learning lessened by degrees with the passage of time, disappearing gradually, although the effect of this first learning has been felt from time to time under special stress and strain throughout the writer's lifetime, especially the tendency in tongue and jaw to move to the right.

To sum up, the actual happenings upon which the writer bases her conviction that the changes in speech movements required in the correction of speech have a real bearing on the problem of stuttering were these:

1. The writer's movements of speech were first learned and habituated according to definite sequences, without any conscious knowledge of how it was done.

2. These first learned movements were changed to a different sequence of movements requiring a different functioning for each sound, word, and sentence.

The results of these changes were as follows:

1. A feeling of uncertainty and instability in the use of the muscles of speech.

2. After the later learned movements were put into an all-time use, there emerged an entirely new experience. The first learned processes came into consciousness in their former locations and activity, timed with the use of the newer patterns, which had become partially habituated. The primary habits came into consciousness as strong forces, determined to function in their previous locations and in the former direction and forms of movement. The actual former functioning was prevented, through concentrated attention to the later learned sequences of movements.

3. Greater difficulty was experienced if the subject were tired or ill.

With the writer's own personal experience as a background, she watched the effect of changes in speech-muscle movements on the part of those with whom she worked. When building up the new sequences to replace the old ones, she saw conflict develop between the two. For ex-

ample, a boy of seven years had, up to that time, said "fink" for "think."
In correction, his tongue end was brought to the edge of his upper teeth
by the use of a tongue depressor. He was taught to sense this position,
as he watched the teacher place her tongue in a similar position. He was
shown that his *tongue* starts the moving as he begins to say "think." He
observed this position in a mirror. The new practice went on daily until
the correct form came readily, when under no strain, during lessons. In
fast daily speech the usual *f* substitute appeared part of the time. One
morning the boy came in, excited, to tell of a trip his father was about to
take, and started out, "I fi-fi-thi-think I am going, too." The teacher
paid no attention to the mistake at the time, but later showed again the
correct moving, during the lesson period. For a few months, the boy
occasionally experienced this conflict as the *th* sound came in speech, but
gradually the correct form became dominant. Does it not seem possible
that his form of stuttering on "think" was related to the fact that he had
learned both forms of muscular activity in response to the same sound
stimulation?

The writer has watched the speech of very young children, as they
change movements unhelped, during the correction of baby talk. The
child who says "tum" instead of "come" for two or three years, and who
develops "primary stuttering," may be found using the tongue end first
and then changing to the back-tongue movement, struggling in this manner, saying, "t-t-c-come." (The writer has found none who start with
other substitutions than the *t* sound when stuttering on the initial sound
of the *k* words.)

Occasionally one finds a stutterer whose lips move to the center first,
as for *oo* in "food," when a word starts with an *l* sound. Little children
often substitute the *w* beginning for the *l*, as "wike" for "like." Consequently, when the change is made blindly, the lips may come to the *oo*
position first, and find it difficult to let go, to start the corrected form
"like." A prolonged *oo*, then a change to *l*, "like," sometimes becomes the
habitual reaction to *l* beginnings.

Here is an example of a young stutterer whose form of stuttering was
apparently a conflict between two learning processes. He started all
sentences beginning with "I" by closing his lips first, and sounding a prolonged *m* sound. Then the lips would part and "I" would emerge. In
consultation with the mother, the writer found that certain forms used in
baby talk had been used into the fourth year. One of these was the use
of the pronoun "me" instead of "I." He said "Me want" instead of "I
want," and the jaw moved habitually upward, allowing the lower lip to
contact the upper as he designated *himself*, by saying "me." These movements, with the accompanying "m" sound, had become habitual. The
change to "I" necessitated the opposite activity of muscles. Now the jaw
had to open instead of close. The first step in therapy was to give the
child a clear mental concept of what he had been doing, compared with

the movement for correction. He was shown that the mouth must open to say "I." The boy was asked to place his hand on his lower jaw and open the mouth with a downward movement, thus getting the feel of this movement, as he began the immediate sounding of "I," followed by words having various beginnings, as "I want," "I see," "I come." This practice was continued until the child reached the point where he would stop deliberately in daily speech to form the "I" and then to complete his sentence—a practice which led to fluent speech within a few months.

Incorrect learning in the use of the jaw may bring uncertainty to jaw activity following "correction." The child who substitutes "the" (voiceless *th*) for "see" for several years, has formed incorrect habits for both tongue and jaw. As the sound of *th* begins, the jaw normally assumes a position which allows the tongue end to come in between the two rows of incisors to contact the upper ones. This is a lower level for the jaw than he will use when he corrects and uses the usual closure for "see." Correction necessitates the bringing upward of the jaw for a space approximating the thickness of the tongue end which has previously separated the jaws. As the tongue is brought inside the jaws in correction, and the lower jaw moves closer to the upper, a vacillating effect may sometimes be noted in jaw action. For example, when an emotional upset came to a certain child whose corrected *s* habit was not stable enough to function under all conditions, the movement of the jaw became an uncontrolled up-down movement, in which he blindly moved from one jaw level to the other, before he struck the corrected level and finally could say "see."

It is not only in the mouth muscles that one may detect irregularities of speech due to unsatisfactory learning. A definite use of the air current is necessary in order to have fluent speech. A close co-ordination between the muscles which bring the air current upward and the mouth muscles is necessary, or speech may be intermittent, halting, or stopped altogether. To illustrate: in one case the intake of air habitually continued after the subject attempted to start speech, constantly expanding at the waistline. A silent struggle would ensue, until the reversal of the waist action was brought about and it was possible to have the use of an outgoing air current.

Another subject always began talking on the incoming current, and then finished her sentence on the outgoing current as she reversed muscular action. She lost her position as saleswoman in a drug store because of her "stuttering." Therapy in her case consisted of a thorough insight into her own speech functioning as compared to the normal. The speech practice consisted of a quick intake of air during a silent period. As soon as this was done, she was shown that the whole sentence could then be spoken from the start on the outgoing current. Placing her hands at the waistline, she guided the action of the muscles consciously. She felt the enlarging action as air came in. She was shown how a certain regulated amount of air for the intake is more conducive to the immediate start of the sentence than if one takes too much, since the starting of speech is timed with the recoil of the muscles inward. In six months she was back in her old position, apparently to the satisfaction of her employer. Her fear of failure had gone. She could face life with confidence now, because she understood how to control the tools of communication, without the constant fear which comes with a lack of understanding of the processes.

A third subject blew all of the air outward before starting a sentence, and then talked painfully on the incoming current. If the right sustained pressure is not exerted by the diaphragm and rib activity at the time that speech begins, the outgoing air current will not be available for the use of speech. (Whenever the dentist wishes to use a current of air to dry a tooth cavity, there is but one way to produce that air. Even, sustained pressure must be exerted against the bulb.) There seems to be a close relationship between the deviations from normal air control and the conflicting habit patterns as they are felt in the mouth. A sudden gasp or irregular breathing sometimes becomes a part of the effort to break the force of the conflicts felt in the mouth activity. Thus a "vicious circle" is begun, and is accentuated by emotion as it continues.

There are certain conditions in individual mouths which tend to produce stumbling speech. It is sometimes difficult for the subject to use his mouth so as to produce a given sound. Open spaces between incisors or certain irregularities in teeth or shape of mouth may bring such difficulty. A case in point was that of a young man of twenty-two years, then a sophomore in college. The molars were able to occlude as the jaw closed, but the incisors were about an eighth of an inch apart. He was called a "stutterer," although his only mistake was one which started the initial *s* sound. Two or three attempts would be made in starting words beginning with *s*, then a third, more forcefully made, completed the word as he was in the habit of saying it. His *s* lacked the essential hissing sound. Upon questioning, he admitted that he had no idea how the *s* sound should be made. He was making it as he had always made it, since childhood. He was then shown how the tongue usually adjusts to the dental ridge for the *s* sound. (See *s* in voiceless consonants.) He was also shown that the opening between his incisors had made this process difficult, and that in his case it had apparently resulted in a struggle over each initial *s* sound. He was shown how a slight readjustment in the use of his tongue might make the effort for *s* simpler and easier, and also bring a better sound. He was shown that he could direct his mouth consciously to assume this corrected position in daily practice until it would become habitual with him, and that he could thereby eliminate this initial struggle.

Being a person of courage and insight, this subject immediately began to practice the correction, and to pause long enough, even in daily speech, to get the adjusted position for the *s* sound. At the end of three weeks, the young man asserted that he needed no more assistance, as he now saw how to overcome his difficulty. About this time his relatives gave him a party, as he was leaving to go back to college. In the course of the evening, they were telling jokes, and as the young man started to tell a story, he hesitated on one of his *s* sounds. He stopped short. "Now you'll all have to wait until I repeat that," he said, "and get that *s* right." He did this, to the appreciation and amusement of all, for he had a keen sense of humor, expressing it in delightful ways in spite of his stuttering. This was his only noticeable error in speech that evening. He knew what to do at this point, whereas all muscular activity for speech had previously functioned automatically as he had grown into it, without any conscious knowledge of how he might change it.

Here is another case in which an adult stutterer was aided by gaining an insight into the normal movements for speech. The subject was a young man of twenty-five years of age, a bank teller. His only mistake came on words beginning with the *k* sound. There would generally be several *t* beginnings, then a *k*, repeated once or twice. Then the whole word, as "t-t-c-c-come," would be given. The teacher asked her subject if he knew the movements of the mouth which start the *k* words. He did not, nor did he know the history of his speech-development days. However, he was shown the normal functioning as "come" begins, shown that the back of the tongue starts the correct movement and that the forward movement, as he was using it, was unnecessary. This forward movement might be discarded in time, by giving the back-tongue stimulation in daily practice, immediately upon closing the word preceding it. An insight into the mistake and its relation to the normal correct procedure was the first step. The next step was a daily stimulation of the back-tongue movement following words which close in various positions of the mouth. This practice built up a new sequence of movements, giving the mouth the feeling of moving at the back of the tongue as the *k* words began, thus consciously discarding the frontal movement, which had habitually preceded the *k* beginning. By the end of six months, largely by his own training, he had overcome the outward stutter, but he said that he often felt the end of his tongue trying to push forward, according to the former habit. He found this tendency annoying, but he had learned to control the situation, so far as the actual movements were concerned. Later he reported that he seldom had any reason to be conscious of his one-time difficulty.

It is the exceptional adult stutterer, though, who can be aided by the application of direct speech aid only. In those cases in which the habitual functioning of muscles opposes the necessary control of a current of air during speech, it has been found helpful to give certain subjects an insight into the meaning of air control. By the time secondary stuttering has arrived, however, the whole condition has usually become so complicated that the average adult stutterer does better to forget the technical production of speech and be aided by those who are skilled in the psychological or psychiatric approach, as it often becomes a personality problem.

All forms of defective speech which are repetitive or stumbling or halting are called "stuttering." However, no two stutterers stutter exactly alike. The muscular difficulties which are seen outwardly, with sometimes extraneous movements, do not appear exactly the same in any two cases. The psychological problems are not the same, either. Each stutterer presents an individual problem. The writer believes that since all of the movements of speech must be learned after birth and co-ordinated according to a definite pattern, there may be mistaken learning in any part of the speech musculature. Wherever there is faulty learning, there is an attempt at correction, often accentuating the mistake already begun. This may account for some of the variations seen in the forms of stuttering. The attempt at correction in childhood is blindly made. The child does not know how his speech mechanism ought to function.

It would seem that all muscular learning for speech, used often enough to form a habit, is stored away in the subconscious mind, and may appear again under certain conditions. If two different responses through movement of muscles have been learned in response to one and the same stimulation, the first learned response remains there, even if it has been replaced. Under favorable conditions the second learning, the correction, becomes dominant. Under certain other less favorable conditions, which may be physiological, environmental, psychological, or a combination of all, the primary learning may break through. Since it was associated with the same stimulation as the corrected learning, under unsatisfactory conditions both forms of learning may attempt to react at the same time at which stimulation appears. Not understanding what is happening to him, the subject is unable to control any part of these movements, but is led on blindly by the various forces which are unleashed within him. These forces appear as tendencies to move muscles in certain previously used locations in the mouth or as a force moving muscles in a certain direction, while other habit patterns are exerted otherwise. The stutterer may say "d-d-d-g-go," a conflicting reaction formed by both habit patterns. Or the two habit patterns may so nearly oppose each other that neither speech pattern is possible, and speech is stopped, until some use of extraneous muscles breaks the deadlock. In the case of the last named conflict, the tongue has learned to go forward for "do," and backward for the start of "go," correctly spoken. If these opposing forces are equal, the tongue cannot move in either direction, and so neither pattern *can* function until the deadlock is broken. The same situation is seen occasionally when the movements for *t* and *k* are in conflict.

The stimulation which becomes associated with definite movements may be a sound, a symbol, or an idea. The first learned muscular response seems to gain a very strong hold upon the use of the muscles, even in the first few years. This becomes very evident when we are working to replace one pattern by another in correction at the age of three years or less. The writer worked with an infant of fourteen months at one time, giving him the stimulations for the words which she felt he would be most apt to use first. She preceded his learning with the correct stimulations for the sound patterns—all but one, the sound of *th*. He toddled into the bathroom one day and went to the tub, looked into it, and said "baf." He was used to the teacher working with him for a few seconds at a time, and she waited until the child was ready for his nap, in a reclining position. She stimulated *ba* and then got his tongue to the edge of his upper teeth, and completed "ba-th." This was repeated several times a week for six months before the child had made the complete change from "baf" to "bath." Every other pattern, which had been stimulated *before* an incorrect one could gain usage, never changed, nor was any attempt made by the child to use other than correct forms except for *th*. The first learned forms are more deeply entrenched than those learned later ; therefore, if disturbed, but not forming a deadlock, these first learned movements start the response, such as the "t-t-c-come," changing to the second learning afterward. The writer has watched for a reversal of the order, as "c-c-t-tum," but has not found it, although the first movement forward to make *t* may have been dropped in some cases in which the stuttering form is "c-c-c-come," leaving only a feeling of uncertainty as the initial *k* approaches.

The strength of these opposing forces, felt in the speech muscles themselves, is not realized by the person who has not felt them himself. It is true that speech habits are equally strong in the person whose speech is normal, but he is not aware of their strength because he is being aided by the force of correct habit formation, as he talks from day to day. The terrific force of opposing habits was not felt by the writer in her youth until she substituted other movements for those already habituated. Since she knew what her own movements had been, and also what she was substituting for them, it was a simple thing for her to recognize former patterns as they appeared. She also recognized the *imperative necessity* of not permitting these first learned forms to function, since she wished to carry the correction to a satisfactory finish. As before stated, the insistent guidance through conscious control was the only means by which the use of the correct sequences was made possible. At this point in her effort, yielding to the demands of the first learning would have meant either the control by the former movements or a mixup of both without hope of correction. It would have meant stumbling speech. Since the two sequences never were permitted to form habitual physical conflict, no patterns of conflicting movements such as are seen in stuttering were built up, in which part of the movements of one pattern appears, and then part of another. The continuous functioning of the new learning went on, under constant direction of the conscious mind, while at the same time a forceful interjection of former patterns was felt in the manner of the first learning. These forces were felt in the exact location of the former functioning, and in the direction and form of the former moving. Thus the mental control, by which the newer learning was kept in use, was made most difficult, and at times all but impossible. However, one factor which aided in the continuity of the newer learning was that its sequences of movements had never been practiced as a part of the former. The two sequences of movements were different, and had been kept apart in practicing, since the newer learning was used only when the writer was alone, practicing; and the former was used in conversation with others. This fact made conscious control more nearly possible, even when the sensations from the speech muscles were doubled, or confused.

The theory of conflict as one of the causes of stuttering is not new. The conflict in some other area than that of the speech muscles themselves has been considered to be indirectly the cause of conflict appearing in the speech muscles, as an outlet for some other form of conflict. "Emotional conflicts," "foreign language conflicts," "parental conflicts," "social conflicts," "mental conflicts," are sometimes given as causes for stuttering. The conflicts just mentioned, as the writer views it, tend to arouse the submerged muscular patterns associated with the first forms used in expression. They tend to aggravate conflicts whose bases are already laid, through previous changes in the use of speech muscles. In "correction," a long perpetuated set of muscle patterns must be displaced or inhibited, while a new set of movements is initiated and must entirely replace the former pattern of reaction. A big step toward the prevention of stuttering would be made if muscular movements for speech could be acquired in the correct way when they are first gained—never to be changed.

THERAPY IN CASES OF PRIMARY STUTTERING

In the writer's work with primary stutterers, her aim has always been, not only to stabilize the emotional life, but to build up stable sequences of movements. Feeling the location of the movement, feeling the teacher's stimulation as to how to move the desired set of muscles, becomes a means of stabilizing speech movements. The stimulation throughout words and sentences guides the muscles into permanent normal functioning. To illustrate: the writer once worked with a child of four years who was stuttering very badly. He repeated most of the initial sounds of words and became completely blocked when words beginning with the *k* sound came into speech. He would then struggle to continue speech, and finally would give one or two hard jerks with his head; then the deadlock would be broken. In the beginning work the teacher's effort was toward establishing rapport and in creating a situation in which the child found an interesting program with other children. Daily he received three or four speech lessons, lasting at first from one to three minutes. The child would climb up the steps of the speech table, recline, receive a few stimulations for correct moving of muscles, starting first with the *k* words. Then he would climb down, go back to the nursery-school program, where speech was not mentioned, but where there was a happy atmosphere in which children did hand work, played games, sang songs, and danced folk dances.[2]

The speech work of the first few months with this child showed slight gain. As time progressed, the head jerk came less often, as the boy found that he could make the *k* beginning in the right place and with the right movements, while his head was motionless. Gradually, other initial beginnings were stabilized, and at the close of eighteen months of training, the child was talking normally. A call at his home, after a period of two years, assured us that there had been no return of stuttering.

The following conclusions, with suggestions on therapy, are given as the result of the writer's work on the problem of primary stuttering:

1. Interference or conflicts in later speech are a possibility where two patterns of muscular learning have been associated with the same stimulation at different periods. (The pattern of baby talk and that for correct speech.) Whether these conflicts come into the open or not depends largely upon psychological, neurological, or environmental factors.

2. The moto-kinesthetic method can be used (together with a sound psychological approach) with therapeutic value in most cases of primary stuttering, if the adult learns the techniques thoroughly. The exact application varies with the case. Until it is thoroughly learned, do not try it. Use only the suggestions offered in the treatise, *Stuttering*.

3. All effort in therapy should work toward stabilizing sequences of movements, both through the psychological approach and the training of muscles. There is therapeutic value in *feeling* the stimulations for movement in the order and sequence desired. There is no value in asking a child to repeat a sentence. Indeed, it has an unstabilizing effect through calling attention to his stuttering, without aiding in the therapy.

4. All stimulations should be given casually, gradually leading the child into wanting the help. The best time to help, unless the situation were such as to bring embarrassment, is at the time of his struggle, preceded at first by some such remark as, "I can help you to say it right." The stimulation is given casually, cheerily, ending occasionally with, "Next time you'll do it better." Then speech is forgotten until the moment for definite help comes again. All is done without worry, because one can have the assurance that speech will be stabilized in time.

5. Wherever there is a repetition of two sounds, for the initial sound of words, as "t-t-c-come," the stimulation of the desired movements helps them to assume dominance. The undesirable are omitted and discarded. The stimulation is given throughout the preceding word followed by the stimulation for the initial sound of the word causing trouble.

6. Wherever there is a repetition of the same sound, as "t-t-t-Tom," the uncertainty is reduced by the frequent application of the one stimula-

---

[2] At the Hill-Young School of Speech, formerly at Los Angeles, California.

tion for the movement which produces the one *t*, followed by the immediate stimulation of the rest of the word.

7. Where there is in-co-ordination between the muscles which control the air and the mouth movements, the young child may be taken on one's lap, with a picture book, and his speech encouraged. As he speaks his sentences, the adult may lay a hand over the child's waistline, pressing inward and upward, as he speaks. She lets go her hold at the intake of the air. She does not mention speech to him. They talk together with interest about the pictures. She does not tell him what to do. She merely lets him *feel* what to do, so as to form correct habits of breathing as they are related to speech output.

8. Stuttering may be minimized by the attitude and training of the adults in charge of children during the speech acquisition period. However, another preventive measure is the gaining of the correct use of speech movements when first talking. The elimination of baby talk to the infant, as well as the use of speech which is not too complicated, on the part of adults, is a factor in correct learning. If speech is well begun in the second year, it is apt to continue to function in a more stable manner than if longer delayed. A careful directing of patterns, which have not come readily into use, hastens the formation of correct habits, and tends toward stabilizing speech.

RESEARCH NEEDED ON SPEECH BEGINNINGS

As the writer sees it, research should be done to show the facts relative to early muscular learning as affecting later speech, while including all possible physiological, environmental, and psychological factors in each case. Research is needed to accomplish these things:

1. To find the facts resulting from the definite training of speech movements when first gained, as compared to allowing the infant to gain it by his own efforts.

2. To establish the facts regarding the results when two or more muscular patterns for speech use are gained and used at different periods of time, in response to one and the same stimulation. This stimulation may be a sound, a written symbol, or an idea.

3. To show the relative ability of the child of one to three years to learn a pattern of movement when stimulated through the kinesthetic sense, as compared to that of older children.

4. To observe the muscular learning of a large group of children, to have the observation extended over a long enough period of time to check the changes after early correction, continuing regular checks through the first year of school adjustment. If any stutter, one should note the forms as compared with his first learned speech movements.

5. To show the effects on the development of mentality and personality when speech is gained early and correctly at the outset.

WHY THE NATURE OF MUSCULAR CONFLICTS HAS NOT BEEN SOLVED

1. The beginnings of speech have not received sufficient attention from the standpoint of the kind of muscular learning involved. In looking for the kind of steps in learning which tend toward stuttering, the emphasis should be placed upon the nature of the muscular learning involved, not upon the progress of sounds used. It is usually taken for granted that baby talk is but a necessary first step in the progress and development of speech. This assumption should be questioned, in view of the possibility of certain hang-overs which may affect later speech.

2. The individual stutterer is not usually in a position to contribute anything constructive to the solving of this possible phase of his difficulty. The child is not conscious of how the beginnings of speech evolved, of what he did in correction, nor why he began to find speech difficult.

3. There is little understanding of the nature and strength of the conflicting forces which occur when the early, primary learning is rearoused and struggles to regain its former activity, after the subject has once made the supposed "correction." Such data must somehow be found in the actual experiences of individuals. These facts are difficult to obtain. Herein lies the writer's feeling of great responsibility, because it is not apt to come into many lives to spend the necessary time in studying out these definite, detailed movements of speech. Necessity was one of the compelling forces in the writer's case, coupled with a challenging interest in working on a problem. It would seem that it does not come often into human experience to feel the beginnings of muscular interference and conflict, while at the same time being in a position through study to recognize the patterns involved in the conflict.

A deep innate responsibility for the facts of such an experience becomes the burden of the individual, from which he cannot escape until he has left his findings for the use and evaluation of others. Herein lies the reason for the writing of this book—an attempt on the part of the writer to fulfill the obligation which the events of life seem to have imposed upon her.

MOTO-KINESTHETIC
SPEECH TRAINING

Part Two

By Sara Stinchfield Hawk

ACKNOWLEDGMENTS

Appreciation is expressed for suggestions received from and for permissions given by the following persons, namely: the staff of the Nursery School for Visually Handicapped Children, Los Angeles, and especially to Dr. Lillian Ray Titcomb, founder-member of the staff and Mrs. Merle Loft, Nursery School Director, for their patience in reading the material on the blind child; to Dr. Samuel Perkins Hayes, Psychologist, Research Director, Perkins Institution, Watertown, Massachusetts, for suggestions regarding the chapter on blind children; to Dr. Kathryn Maxfield, College of the City of New York and American Foundation for the Blind, former director of the Arthur Sunshine Home for Blind Babies at Summit, New Jersey, for information regarding work in general for blind children; to Mrs. Marie Tappendorff, Director, Cedars Development School, Ross, California, for use of material regarding pupils studied by the writer as psychologist in her school; to graduate student, Herman Pieters, Claremont Graduate College, for advice and assistance on the statistical portion of Chapter Eighteen.

CHAPTER FIFTEEN

DELAYED SPEECH DEVELOPMENT

Scientific interest in defects of speech has led from general attention to the vast field of such disorders to an intensive study of special problems in speech defects. Among these the study of infant speech acquisition, with its frequent delays or disorders in the early formative years, is now beginning to receive detailed study. In order to understand the genesis of speech disorders it is imperative that they should be studied in the early, incipient stages, before the speech mechanism has become too thoroughly habituated to imperfections or to difficulties in utterance. We are here interested in the problem of the child who does not readily acquire speech, or who perhaps entirely fails to develop speech responses at the age when most children have become fairly fluent in self-expression through speech.

Investigations show that speech acquisition is an extremely compli-cated process which unfolds gradually, the periods mentioned by psychol-ogists[1] merging into each other, and varying in time requirements and fluency with different children. The accessory muscles associated with speech must be brought under control after the nerves governing the use of the larger, fundamental muscles have suitably matured and have begun to function in gross muscle movements. The adjustments necessary for speech are much more delicate and difficult to control than are those re-quired for arm and leg movements.

CHARACTERISTICS OF INFANT SPEECH

Children do not acquire language as an adult learns a foreign lan-guage, by learning each word separately with its meaning and then form-ing a sentence. A child learns an entire expression, memorizes it, and "springs it" on its listener at an appropriate time or even out of context. It learns "Oh, my feet are killing me," and then waits for an opportunity to say it. It hears an adult say, "Mrs. Smith has left her husband," alters it slightly, and, though not understanding, it says, "I left my husband yesterday." Thus the child actually builds up its language in the form of *expressions* as units, instead of *words* as units.

Before speech has advanced to the stage of abstract thinking required in adult life, it must begin with the concrete, subjective, and emotional language processes common to childhood and infancy. The infant is egocentric in the majority of his interests and activities.[2] It requires about

[1] W. Stern, *The Psychology of Early Childhood* (New York: Henry Holt & Co., 1930).
[2] Jean Piaget, *The Language and Thought of the Child* (New York: Harcourt, Brace & Co., 1926).

117

two years for him to complete the process of forming the necessary bonds or associations between sounds heard, objects seen, and the motor pattern of movement necessary for translating his ideas into articulate speech. In neurological terms, we must not expect speech to progress very far until the great pyramidal tracts from the motor areas of the brain to remote parts of the body have been properly myelinated. Along with expressive activities of the arms and legs go facial expression and the desire for social participation through articulate speech, which is a distinguishing characteristic of the human race.

There are indications that early efforts at speech, such as we find in the random, spontaneous babbling of the infant, are not directly under the control of the super-motor areas of the brain but occur as a result of a sort of "circular imitation," as Allport has stated,[3] in which the stimulus-response patterns which motivate speech seem to involve the second trophic realm of the nervous system, in the brain stem and cerebellum, rather than the third or highest level. If this is true, early sounds are spontaneous, random, and accidental reactions of the child to human environment, and almost any stimulus is sufficient to touch off a response once the maturing of the nervous system has reached the required level of development. This would account for the babbling of the deaf child, which is a secondary rather than a primary form of speech, even though it eventually leads to the establishment of controls, inhibition of unnecessary articulations, and selection of desired speech sounds out of a mass of early, confused, random, and meaningless impressions.

AUDITORY IMPERCEPTION

When the child begins to apply words meaningfully, we know that he not only is learning to talk but is actually expressing ideas. Although the child who develops in accordance with Nature's plan gains control of the fundamental muscles so that he begins to develop speech sounds in the second half of the first year, the child who suffers from some form of mental, physiological, or emotional retardation may be very slow in the development of control of his neuromuscular mechanism. Facial expression is often an index to the beginnings of active mental life and the dawn of intelligence in the child. The more active functioning of the association areas of the brain leads to development of the muscles of expression in the face and eyes. Because of a lack of such expression in children who have not learned to talk, clinicians and parents sometimes falsely assume that they are feeble-minded. It is unfortunately true that if speech development is long delayed in such cases, and no attempt is made to counteract the effect of a special handicap such an auditory inacuity, deafness, glandular disorder, birth injury, or unfavorable environment, the child may become permanently retarded mentally. These are really matters concerning

---

[3] G. Allport, *Social Psychology* (Boston: Houghton Mifflin Co., 1924).

neuronal patterns or engrams in the central nervous system, and these develop with education, learning, and experience.

It is often impossible to assign an intelligence quotient (IQ) to a child who has been subject to slow development from birth or to one who is a victim of birth injury or adventitious children's diseases, because such a child cannot express himself through the medium of speech. Such a child may have normal perceptions and a very clear idea of what he wishes to say and yet be unable to communicate his ideas to others. His insight and understanding are very different in quality from those of a child who is mentally deficient and who does not perceive meanings.[4]

Certain technical terms are used for designating the defects which may develop. In the case of an actual brain lesion or injury, the speech defect represents a form of "dysarthria," since there is a disorder in the actual production of speech movements. If there is no speech at all, we speak of the disorder as "anarthria." In case there is a special developmental defect, in which the intelligence is unimpaired, the speech defect may vary from complete lack of speech, or "alalia," to baby talk, "infantile perseverance," babbling, and "lalling" or jargon speech, all of which may be classed as forms of "dyslalia," that is, disorders in actual talking, or lallation.[5] Many children who have been diagnosed as speechless lack some of the characteristics of aphasics. True aphasia seems to be largely a disorder of adulthood which, like dementia, rarely appears in childhood. Adult aphasia differs etiologically from that found in childhood, and it is possible that child cases commonly pronounced aphasic belong rather to the group which we shall attempt to describe.[6] The need of differentiation between these types has been discussed by Ewing in his volume on *Aphasia in Children*.[7] Broca described verbal "amnesia" as a form of speech disorder in which the patient pronounced words but could not recall memories for spoken or written words.[8]

The child who is born deaf or who suffers from adventitious deafness at an early age before speech habits have been well established is usually

[4] C. K. Ogden and I. A. Richards, *The Meaning of Meaning* (New York: Harcourt, Brace & Co., 1937).

[5] S. M. Stinchfield, *Speech Disorders* (New York: Harcourt, Brace & Co., 1933).

[6] Samuel D. Robbins, *A Dictionary of Speech Pathology and Therapy* (Cambridge, Mass.: Sci-Art Publishers, 1951).

[7] A. W. Ewing, *Aphasia in Children* (London: Oxford Medical Publications, 1930), pp. 31–48, 77–110.

[8] Henry Head, *Aphasia and Kindred Disorders of Speech*, Vol. I (New York: The Macmillan Company, 1936); also P. Broca, "Sur le siége de la faculté 'du langage articule' avec deux observations d'aphémie," *Bulletin de la société Anatomique de Paris*, August 1861.

known as a deaf-mute, as he develops no speech at all, beyond primitive sounds, or his dyslalia is so marked that his speech is wholly or largely unintelligible. Since he cannot hear the sounds of speech with any degree of accuracy, he imitates them imperfectly or not at all, and his speech is a sort of jargon of primitive sounds, uttered in a toneless, monotonous voice, bearing little resemblance to the articulate speech of the normal child. Such a child lacks the autocritical power of sound-analysis and self-correction which is associated with normal hearing, and he must receive special training not only in lip reading and phonetics but also in the process of voice placement, in voice building, and in the mechanical production of speech sounds in the correct order and sequence in words. Being able to read, to spell, and to write is not sufficient, because many of our spoken words in English bear little phonetic resemblance to their written form. The mastery of speech depends upon training the memory functions associated with visual, auditory, motor, and kinesthetic impressions, so that the sight of a word in print, its appearance on the lips when being pronounced, and the various associations which have been built up around that word may be sufficient to set in motion the memory factors necessary to the actual reproduction of the word by the individual. When the hearing defect is slight, it often remains unrecognized by parents or teachers for years. Important time is thus lost educationally in many cases, owing to the lack of early recognition of the facts of deafness or auditory inacuity or imperception. Schools for the deaf are therefore giving increased attention to the matter of home education of the preschool deaf child, realizing the importance of beginning the process of training during the important years of early childhood. Private schools for the preschool-aged deaf child have also been established.

AUDITORY INACUITY

The importance of normal hearing for speech development is not generally recognized, and there are many children in school today who are classed as dull, inefficient, and inattentive, or even as educationally retarded, without the educator or the parent having discovered the fact of an auditory impairment or auditory inacuity. Serious impairment stands a good chance of being discovered, but in cases of mild impairment, weak auditory imagery, or inacuity in the perception of sounds there is a very good chance that the child's defect may remain undetected unless accidentally revealed. Parents and children, moreover, who are aware of the existence of a slight hearing impairment are often hesitant about mentioning the fact to teacher or principal, and there are, unfortunately, teachers who, even when informed of the condition, do not use such knowledge to the best advantage. On the contrary, the teacher's attitude toward the child and his handicap often only further increases the child's feelings of helplessness and inadequacy and may thereafter prevent the child from communicating the fact of his deafness to other teachers. This places him at a disadvantage throughout his educational career and often into adult life, for sensitivity engendered by treatment in childhood usually persists and may even become intensified with the passing of the years. It is tragic that this should be the case, because it is unnecessary, is unsound psychologically, and involves poor mental hygiene for the individual who is afflicted with a speech or hearing handicap.

DELAYED SPEECH AND APHASIA

In the past, children with delayed speech have been discussed chiefly by writers on aphasia and allied disorders, and there exists an extensive literature on the subject. The close correspondence between delays in speech development and some types of aphasia is mentioned in current literature by such writers as Gutzmann and Flateau in Berlin, Nadoleczny in Munich, Ewing in England, and Appelt, Franz, Fröschels, and Orton in the United States.

In the child of normal hearing, the auditory impressions and pleasurable sensations associated with it are sufficient to arouse the internal adjustments necessary to excite the motor areas associated with overt speech responses. Reflex arcs which are stimulated simultaneously arouse several co-ordinated chains of reflexes, and a speech response occurs. When the cortical areas which exercise an inhibitory function are injured, the interference with inhibition may cause echolalia, which bears some resemblance to certain types of aphasia in which inhibitory functions are lacking, and we have repetitive sounds. In the lallation of infancy much the same thing occurs. The child's spontaneous lalling gives a pleasurable sensation, a sort of circular imitation of self occurs, and this is repeated many times, without meaning, before there is any attempt at imitation of external speech. The writings of these various authorities lead to the conclusion that it is important for us to begin at the early stages of speech initiation to develop the child's responses to auditory stimuli, so that from occasional responses to external stimuli he may learn very quickly to make responses with increasing frequency and finally to respond invariably to certain stimuli. This is, in effect, building up conditioned responses.[9]

Writers on aphasia, following Broca, have usually classified children with delayed speech as aphasics, and much work on localization is described in the literature of Broca with attempts at delimitation of very definite cortical areas or zones within which the difficulty might be said to have occurred.

Pierre Marie made a notable departure from the generally accepted theories when he maintained that possibility of localization was exceedingly doubtful in a great many cases, and he advanced the concept of more generalized cortical control for all mental functions. He was the

[9] E. Fröschels, *Psychological Elements in Speech* (Boston: Expression Co., 1932), pp. 67–139.

first to oppose the theory that the third frontal convolution played a specially important role in speech functions. Marie and his pupil Moutier called attention to the fact that delayed speech (dyslalia or actual alalia) often existed where there was no indication of actual paralysis or lesion. Moutier called attention to the individual variations found in children with delayed speech, as varying anywhere from total absence of any articulate speech to fragments of words, babbling, "idiolalia," jargon speech, and baby talk or "infantile perseverance." Many patients were reported by Moutier as possessing normal intelligence but suffering from motor–in-co-ordination and anarthria. Often the anarthria was found to be combined with symptoms of aphasia.[10]

Head[11] postulated four types of aphasia: (1) verbal, (2) syntactic, (3) nominal, and (4) semantic. In verbal aphasia, inner speech is disturbed, as well as overt expression. The syntactic is largely jargon speech, although the patient can read, draw, and write, which functions are lost or disturbed in verbal aphasia. In nominal aphasia there is amnesia for spoken commands, reading aloud, audible speech, and comprehension of word meanings. In semantic aphasia, details are grasped and understood by the patient but are not united to form entire concepts; the connection between details and their relations to the whole is not grasped.

Von Monakow departs from rigid theories of localization and maintains that functional integration is disturbed by diffused disturbances which involve the various sensory and motor processes. The aphasia, he says, may be a transitory symptom resulting in an inhibition of function rather than in an actual lesion. He speaks of this process as "diaschisis." When the diaschisis has passed or been overcome by re-education or training, functional normality is present. This is the more satisfactory explanation from the standpoint of educability of speechless children.[12]

PSYCHOLOGICAL CONTRIBUTIONS

On the psychological side there were the brilliant contributions of Hinshelwood[13] to the literature on word-blindness or "alexia" in the early part of this century, to which has been added more recently the result of important researches on "dyslexia" by Hincks, Lord, and Dearborn from the psychological laboratories of the Harvard Graduate School of Education, of Orton at the New York Neurological Center, of Travis at the State University of Iowa, and of Monroe, of the University of Chicago. In the past few years there has been much important research on children with reading disabilities. The relation between dyslexia, or

[10] Pierre Marie, "Revision de la question de l'aphasie," *Semana Médica* (Buenos Aires), May 23, 1906; François Moutier, *L'Aphasie de Broca* (Paris: G. W. Steinheil, 1908).

[11] Henry Head, *Aphasia* (New York: The Macmillan Company, 1936), Vol. I.

[12] C. von Monakow, *Gehirnpathologie*, second edition (Wien: A. Hölder, 1905).

[13] J. Hinshelwood, "Congenital Word-Blindness," *Lancet*, Vol. LXXVIII (1900).

reading, writing, and spelling difficulties, and allied speech defects has been described by Fernald in her work at the University of California at Los Angeles. Earlier clinical theories of localization of speech centers, such as had been postulated by Broca and Wernicke, seem to have been largely discarded by workers in the field of aphasia today. That is, while definite areas of the cortex topographically represent "controls" for various parts of the body, speech is based upon a much more complicated mechanism. While there are many forms of aphasia in which loss of speech is associated with lesions of the brain, there are now believed to be many cases of delayed speech, "congenital word-deafness and word-blindness," in which there exists no actual lesion but rather a reduction in cortical control or a suspension of cortical activity or an insensitivity of certain cortical areas to ordinarily adequate stimuli, which may be temporary or permanent, depending upon the effectiveness of therapeutic measures instituted, the time which elapses before corrective educational measures are applied, the ability of the child to respond, and methods employed by the worker. While these recent theories complicate our understanding of the problem of speech development, it is much more hopeful than is the thesis of earlier authorities, who held firmly to the theory of speech delay or absence of speech as almost invariably a form of aphasia.

Pick maintains[14] that articulate speech takes place as a result of superimpositions of earlier and later functions in layer-like fashion. The process becomes extremely complicated. It is probable that the cortical areas involved in the simple utterance of a meaningful word may involve not merely a single, restricted, "localized" area, but rather many adjacent areas of the brain, the sensory and motor mechanisms being correlated in their activity, only after many, many experiences in forming associations between the sight of objects, the touching and manipulating of objects, cutaneous and tactual impressions of them, the sound of them, and the oft-repeated names associated with each object, after many efforts at tagging, through the process of memory fixation. This is in line with Gestalt psychology.

Goldstein maintains that pleasurable sensations accompany the speech movements and cause the child to move its speech muscles. Articulate, meaningful speech, he says, occurs only after an association has been formed between definite words and definite experiences.[15]

Stern calls attention to the rhythmic, wave-like movement of speech development in which alternate periods of rapid progress and of slow learning occur. The child's energy cannot encompass mastery of all of the needed functions at once.[16] The infant's selection of words may be

[14] A. Pick, "Zur Frage nach der Natur der Echolalie," *Fortschritte der Psychologie*, Bd. 4, H. 1.
[15] J. Goldstein, *Die transkortikalen Aphasien* (Jena, 1915).
[16] C. and W. Stern, *Kindersprache* (Leipzig, 1907).

in accordance with the urge to communicate with his environment, or to develop his interests more fully, or in accordance with mental maturation and physical growth. These lead to entirely different quantitative and qualitative speech structures in different children, even in the same family and environment.

Meumann speaks[17] of the emotional-volitional stage in infant speech as followed by the intellectualizing stage. The latter is the associative-reproductive period, when ideation becomes more abstract, while earlier speech is largely concrete and egocentric. Some children never progress beyond the first stage.

Bluemel[18] applies the principles of the conditioned reflex to the establishment of speech responses in children. He calls attention to the work of Pavlov, who maintains that associations are physiological rather than psychological and cites examples from Pavlov's experimental work with dogs to show the physiological nature of certain responses ordinarily believed to be entirely of a psychological nature. He found that his dogs could be conditioned to artificial as well as to natural stimuli; that is, they responded by salivary-gland action not only at sight of the natural stimulus (food, dishes, bowl, etc.) but also to an artificial stimulus which they had learned to associate with the natural stimulus, such as a whistle, a horn, a light, or the experimenter himself. The dogs could be conditioned to changes in intensity of sound and to cessation of sound, as well as to changes in intervals between interrupted tones. They learned to respond to both visual and auditory stimuli. This is important from the standpoint of motor and kinesthetic images in speech.

The unconditioned response is the normal or natural response which the organism makes to a given stimulus. The conditioned response is one in which the organism adjusts itself to some change in the situation, calling for some association between the original stimulus and the new element in the situation, such that an automatic reaction occurs immediately upon application of the altered stimulus or on substitution of the new stimulus in place of the original stimulus.

According to Bluemel, the acquisition of language is a conditioned response, as are reading and writing. These are spoken of as arbitrary, local, and variable, the child being required to learn them after much practice and many experiences of associating them with objects in his environment.

PAVLOV'S EXPERIMENTS

Pavlov's experiments throw important light on speech reactions, showing how easily an established response may be checked, inhibited, or altered by complicating the situation. When conditions are sufficiently

[17] E. Meumann, *Psychology of Learning* (New York: D. Appleton Co., 1913).
[18] C. S. Bluemel, *Stammering and Allied Disorder* (New York: The Macmillan Company, 1935), pp. 4–25.

altered, the experimental animal becomes extremely irritable, and even breaks down under the strain of an increasingly complex situation. When positive and negative stimuli are sufficiently varied to enable the animal to distinguish between them without great difficulty, the response is immediate and satisfying; but when the situation is altered and the gradations of difference between positive and negative stimuli are very slight, the dog becomes nervous and irritable, and may even go to pieces, much as a human being might do in a complicated speech situation.

Bluemel shows that when speech responses are imperfect and unstable, as in infancy, it requires very little to upset the delicate balance and to throw the child's nervous system into much the same state of chaos and confusion as we find in the experimental animals aforesaid.[19] He further establishes that, if inhibitory tendencies are strongly developed in children, the conditioned response to speech stimuli may fail to develop and this early inhibition of the speech impulses may lead to permanent retardation.

That the infant speech mechanism is very susceptible to inhibitory influences is seen from such experiments as those mentioned. The importance of normal health and favorable conditions also is indicated from the results of Pavlov's experiments. The child in the early emotional period of speech development is immature physically and mentally, and it takes very little to upset the balance of the finely adjusted sensory and motor associative areas which function in speech. There may be a partial or total inhibition of the speech impulses, due to unfavorable factors in the environment, or undue excitation may render the child extremely neurotic or negativistic.

DEVELOPMENTAL DISORDERS

The surprising response to training observed in a number of children who have been variously diagnosed as feeble-minded or subnormal, and as paralytics, as mutes, as totally deaf, as victims of brain injury at birth, as postencephalitics, as meningitics, and as aphasics in many cases throws doubt upon the accuracy of the common prognosis. Of course there exist speech defects in practically all of these disorders or failures in development; but there are cases of speech defects commonly attributed to these etiological factors which apparently belong in none of these categories. They are rather developmental failures or cases in which there are anomalies of mental or physical development, temporary arrests of cerebral development, or retarded mental growth which may be far more hopeful, educationally, than the early prognosis indicates. We are especially interested in cases where there exists some retardation in mental unfoldment, some arrest of psychic growth, or some lack of development of the associational life of a child such that the child is unable to acquire speech through the usual auditory channels. Were there a central lesion, such

[19] Bluemel, *op. cit.*, p. 46.

children would be unable to acquire normal speech, and tests of audition should indicate that there is a nerve deafness or a central lesion, or defect in the outer or in the middle ear. This would account for inability to understand those parts of language which contain tones of low frequency, whereas nerve deafness or a central defect in the auditory perceptual region should be indicated by inability to understand tones of high frequency. Improvement obtained in many instances shows that such is not the case.

Workers in the field of speech pathology and clinical and psychological investigators into causes of speech anomalies find that there are children reared in an apparently normal environment and having a clear health record who fail to develop speech into the second or third year. Gesture may be present and powers of mimetic expression of a subjective type, but the child lacks the power of articulate speech or is exceedingly backward in speech development for a child of its age. The increasing frequency with which such cases are being brought to our attention, in speech clinical work with preschool or young children, is the reason for our present investigation and for presentation of methods of speech therapy, described by Mrs. Young in Part One.

NORMAL SPEECH DEVELOPMENT

In normal speech we have the building up of associations in response to social stimuli. The acquisition of speech is a psychophysical process in which associations are gradually built up between the audio-sensory, visuosensory, kinesthetic, and motor sensations and the memory patterns or images which these impress upon the mind of the child through repetition, vividness of impression, intensity, nature of the stimuli, and similar advantageous factors. If these occur with sufficient intensity or frequency, they normally make an impression upon the plastic mind of the young child during the period when it yields most readily and easily to such sensory impressions. Normal speech develops out of a mass of these auditory, visual, motor, and kinesthetic impressions and images, each contributing its share to the composite pattern which is first a part of the child's understanding of language and later a part of his own reactions through imitation of speech sounds, mimetic gestures, and direct contact with his environment through the medium of speech.

A child may be entirely normal and yet may depend upon visual, motor, and kinesthetic factors more than upon auditory factors in speech development. Because he is relatively unresponsive to auditory stimuli he may fail to develop speech at the most favorable time. Speech may even be delayed for several years, owing to the child's inability to respond to auditory stimuli and his apparent inability to make normal use of such stimuli for the development of language and communication. Whether such an inability is due to hereditary, congenital, or acquired characteristics or whether the explanation is an environmental one is not clearly understood. Indications are that the problem is exceedingly complicated and that delayed speech may be due to either physiological or psychological causes or to a combination of both. It may also be due to innate trait differences in children, lack of sensitivity to auditory or visual stimuli, and habits of attention which focus upon motor and kinesthetic impressions, rather than upon visual and auditory images. Undoubtedly some children are motor-minded.

In recent studies on speech development and the pathology of speech, Orton[20] discusses emotional language as largely instinctive and unlearned, whereas symbolic language is highly complex. Emotive and gestural language are more primitive forms of expression in which one needs little or no training; but in verbal expression all language must be acquired by a difficult process of learning, whether it be in reading, in writing, or in spoken language. Orton has stressed another factor, which agrees with our findings on nursery-school children, namely, that those children who are delayed in speech may continue to use emotional expression over a longer period and more generally than the child who develops articulate speech normally. He has found, as have we, wide individual variations in the acquisition of language, depending on inherent differences in the psychology or the physiology of the child. Orton believes that the cortices of the angular gyrus may not have been sufficiently developed at six years in some children for reading readiness to be present, while in others whose development proceeds more rapidly this readiness may appear at or before the age of six years.

Newer concepts of speech support our contention that there may be also a period of speech readiness, at the onset of which and for some months following, spoken language may be most readily acquired by the young child. While it varies widely in different children in the same family and delay is not to be considered as a form of intellectual retardation, it is probable that the development of the motor and sensory areas of the brain where speech impressions are stored proceeds at very different rates in different children, so that some seem precocious as compared with other children in the same family group. This is borne out by the researches at the Babies' Hospital, at the Medical Center in New York, where McGraw[21] reports on progressive changes in the vocalizations of infants during the first year of life. Phonographic recordings of the cries of infants show progressive development in the strength and power of the expressive cries, and changes in the quality and pitch in later months as compared with the cries first recorded.

McGraw also finds that the most favorable time to perfect the natural swimming movements of a child is found in infancy, as the baby when placed in water, at the age of nine to fourteen months, will actually swim,

[20] S. Orton, *Reading, Writing, and Speech Problems in Children* (New York: W. W. Norton, 1937), pp. 13–20.
[21] M. McGraw, *Growth* (New York: Appleton-Century Co., 1935).

although not able to hold its head above water. The infant loses this ability soon after the fourteenth month, and then responds much more slowly, with greater elements of fear and uncertainty. In a corresponding way, we have found that children develop speech most normally when given encouragement and direction at the age when the speech readiness first begins to be apparent, with the attempt to name objects or to designate them in words. This is close upon the end of the first year in the average child, but may appear as early as the ninth month in precocious children, and is likely to continue active to about the eighteenth month. With the coming of the second birthday, or around the twenty-fourth month, the most favorable period for speech development may have passed, so that speech subsequently develops much more slowly and with less facility than when it is begun earlier. It is important that parents and nurses should recognize this period of speech readiness, so that the child may be aided in developing the instrument of speech through social contacts, strengthening of motor and sensory impressions, and deepening of the sensibilities through kinesthetic imagery and experience.

SPEECH PATHOLOGY

Monroe[22] has found that under unfavorable conditions, or even when confronted merely by a wrong attitude on the part of teacher, parent, or child, there is often a withdrawal by the child from the difficult situation. Daydreaming may take the place of action, and unsocial and even delinquent behavior may appear. The child may seek compensation in other fields, feeling hopelessly defeated; he may become tense and excitable to a pathological degree, or he may be helped to attack his problem constructively and finally to overcome his difficulty. These findings apply with equal force to the problem of speech personality associated with difficulty in self-expression, in learning to talk, to vocalize readily, or to find a vocabulary which is sufficient for one's actual needs.

In discussing cerebral localization Nielsen[23] mentions the generally accepted theory that some children are predominantly visual-minded and others auditory-minded, while still others tend to be motor-minded. He finds that a lesion in a guiding center causes far more difficulty than a lesion in a minor center. He finds a close connection between motor aphasia and ideokinetic apraxia associated with language. Writers and laymen often confuse psychological and physiological concepts in dealing with language problems. Anatomical structure of the brain-in-action involves physiological concepts; but the brain considered from a functional standpoint involves psychological concepts. Since in the general speech clinic we seem to be dealing more frequently with psychological concepts

---

[22] M. Monroe and B. Backus, *Remedial Reading* (Boston: Houghton Mifflin Co., 1937), pp. 1–33.

[23] J. M. Nielsen, *Agnosia, Apraxia, and Aphasia* (Los Angeles: Neurological Society of Los Angeles, 1936).

of the speech function, we need to keep these distinctions in mind, especially inasmuch as the psychological cases usually present the more hopeful prognoses for speech workers. The differences are illustrated by the following types of speech losses: First, there may be the inability to emit sounds, as in subcortical aphasia. The difficulty may be psychological, however, as in hysterical mutism. Second, there may be an inability to recognize what one sees, as in visual agnosia. The difficulty may be due to a psychological difficulty which we call "hysterical amblyopia." Third, one may be unable to recall names of objects; this may be a case of amnesic aphasia, or it may be merely simple forgetfulness.

The necessity for adapting tests of intelligence to specially handicapped children has been stressed by Lord,[24] who finds that failure to give the correct answers to many questions often is due to a lack of opportunity to learn in a restricted environment, due, that is, to the nature of the handicap, rather than to mental dullness. She finds that standardized tests, with a composite score, may conceal abilities and disabilities which form the crux of the educational problem. The situation in which the child fails and the situation in which he succeeds may teach us more about the child's actual possibilities than any standardized test. The actual mental age at the time of beginning treatment may prove to be unimportant as compared with careful records of the child's actual possibilities and powers of learning over a longer period of observation. Continued treatment and application of remedial measures may change the mental horizon to the point where the child shows considerable improvement in his IQ, as we have found.

SPEECH TRAINING

Monroe[25] suggests some useful educational devices for remedial treatment of young children who present language difficulties or who make low scores on language tests. Beginning with speech tests, she would continue treatment by helping the child to overcome his specific difficulties on various sounds. He may be aided in this through control of the motor movements in speech, through reciting familiar rhymes and jingles, and through repeating the words, slowly at first and gradually with greater rapidity as fluency is gained. She finds that choral speaking is often helpful to the child. Imitation of the sounds made by animals or objects is useful; playing games which require the use of different vocal qualities and changes of pitch are advocated for voice and ear training. Repetition of rhymes and jingles until they are correctly repeated is mentioned.

We have found, as has Monroe, that for children of bilingual background or foreign parentage it is helpful for the child to make up his own

[24] E. Lord, *Children Handicapped by Cerebral Palsy* (New York: Commonwealth Fund, 1937), pp. 26–41.

[25] M. Monroe, *Suggestions for Remedial Reading* (Pittsburgh, Pa.: Pittsburgh Public Schools, 1937).

picture book. With our own cases we have done this, using pictures for
all the sounds of speech found in the English alphabet or selecting the
sounds on which the child has difficulty and building up a picture book
around these sounds, labeling the pictures, talking about them, discussing
situational elements involved, and using the pictures in various ways as
a helpful educational device. For spastic children this method has the
advantage of training the child to use his hands, and to observe and to
select pictures, colors, forms, and appropriate objects which will increase
his experience and add to his knowledge. Special cards have been developed to illustrate each sound in the English language for testing purposes.[26]

The work of Rogers and Thomas[27] has shown how games and play
may be adapted to the needs of the child handicapped by cerebral palsy.
The relationship between singing and speaking has been utilized by them
in exercises in singing and choral work, group and individual. They have
developed exercises for lip movements as in speaking, breathing exercises
through blowing, imitation of sounds made by animals and objects or
people. Games and jingles from various sources are used.[28] We have
found useful a rather simple and inexpensive adaptation of nursery rhymes
in which the teacher and child both participate, the teacher giving the more
difficult words and the child saying the easier words. Thus:

Teacher	*Child*
"This little pig went to ————"	"market."
"This little pig stayed at ————"	"home."
"This little pig had roast ————"	"beef."
"This little pig had ————"	"none."

Other rhymes may be adapted to the special needs of the child, stressing the sounds or words on which he needs practice, by having him fill in
the vacant spaces, as the teacher reads or recites the poem.[29]

SUMMARY

1. In the past, children with unusual difficulty in learning to talk and
to read have usually been classified in medical and psychological literature
as aphasics. The sensory defect has been called "word-dumbness," "word-
blindness," or "word-deafness," and described as appearing in cases which
did not readily respond to auditory or visual stimuli at the age when most
children learn to read and to write.

---

[26] S. Stinchfield, *Handy-Pack Cards* (Chicago: C. H. Stoelting Co., 1937).
[27] G. Rogers and L. Thomas, *New Pathways for Children with Cerebral Palsy*
(New York: The Macmillan Company, 1935).
[28] S. Barrows and K. Hall, *Games and Jingles* (Boston: Expression Co., 1936).
[29] S. S. Hawk, *Speech Therapy for the Physically Handicapped* (Stanford, Calif.:
Stanford University Press, 1950).

2. Unintelligible babbling and lalling has been attributed to a breakdown in the inhibitory functions of the cerebral mechanism.

3. Owing to failures in the establishment of connections between groups of neurones, there may be a partial or a complete inhibition of the speech impulse.

4. The development of normal speech is comparable with Pavlov's conception of conditioned responses.

5. The delicacy of the speech mechanism renders it possible to disturb its fine adjustments very easily.

6. The infant's selection of words may be in accordance with desire to communicate within his environment, within the range of his limited interests, or in accordance with mental and physiological maturation, at appropriate levels of growth. Conditions vary widely even in so-called "similar" environments, because of the variations within the child himself, and because of innate factors which lead to entirely different qualitative and quantitative responses in children of the same family, the same social heritage, and the same environment.

7. If the impulse to talk is not aroused during the normal emotional-volitional stage experienced by most infants, there may be an arrest at an infantile level. The advance from the emoto-volitional stage to the associative-reproductive stage of abstract thinking may be permanently retarded, as a result of fixation in speech development, at an infantile level. Such an arrest is preventable through directing the muscular processes.

8. Moto-kinesthetic speech training is important, so that muscle training and visual and auditory patterns may all be associated in the learning process.

CHAPTER SIXTEEN

ANALYSIS OF PHYSICAL EXAMINATIONS, SPEECH TESTS, AND MENTAL TESTS

CAUSES OF DELAYED SPEECH

Many children are referred to psychiatric, psychological, and speech clinics because of difficulty in learning to talk, to read, to spell, or to write. Sometimes there is found in the same individual difficulty in all four of these fields. This is not surprising in view of the close connection between these functions, and the necessity of building up connections or associations between the eye-hand and the speech-motor processes, as in writing, speaking, or reading. Faulty perceptions may be chiefly in the visual field or in the auditory field or in the motor-speech field or in the formation of associations between any or among all of these. The defect may be chiefly sensory, or chiefly motor or moto-sensory; and associational delimitation of the cortical area or areas involved is often impossible or extremely difficult to define. Whether there is a cortical difficulty or a subcortical transmission defect cannot always be determined even by the most painstaking examination and research on the part of specialists in neurology.

Disabilities in reading, writing, and spelling have been described by research workers in the Harvard Graduate School of Education, and notable contributions to the literature have been made by Lord, Carmichel, and Dearborn,[1] and by Hincks.[2] Excellent results have been obtained with children in the vicinity of Boston as a result of remedial work done in this laboratory.

Through the work of Orton[3] and Travis[4] in the laboratories of the State University of Iowa important contributions have been made to the literature on reading, writing, handedness, spelling, and speech disabilities. Fernald, of the University of California at Los Angeles,[5] has written on spelling and reading disabilities, stressing the fact that speech defects occurring in conjunction with these special defects often clear up without

[1] E. Lord, L. Carmichel, and W. F. Dearborn, *Special Disabilities in Learning to Read and Write* (Harvard Monographs in Education, Ser. 1, Vol. II, No. 1, June 1925).

[2] E. M. Hincks, *Disability in Reading and Its Relation to Personality* (Harvard Graduate School of Education, 1926); also *Disability in Learning to Read in Relation to Neurosis* (Harvard Monographs in Education, Ser. 1, Vol. II, No. 2, 1926).

[3] S. Orton, "Special Disability in Spelling," *Bulletin of the Neurological Institute* (New York), June 1931; also "Familiar Occurrence of Disorders in Acquisition of Language," *Eugenics*, III (April 1930), 4.

[4] L. E. Travis, *Speech Pathology* (New York: D. Appleton Co., 1931).

[5] G. M. Fernald, *Remedial Techniques in Basic School Subjects* (New York: McGraw-Hill Book Company, Inc., 1943).

special speech training and as a result of remedial work on the special difficulty in writing, reading, and spelling. Evidently skill in phonetic analysis and increased comprehension of the meaning or exact values of speech sounds are greatly increased by remedial reading training. This is an important fact because it bears out our observations as to the genesis of many types of speech disorder which are intimately related to inaccurate powers of observation, auditory inacuity, weak auditory perceptions, and consequent faulty motor adjustments of the child in learning to talk.

Because of the frequency with which children with delayed speech and difficulties in learning to read, write, and spell have been referred to nursery schools of Los Angeles with which the writer is associated, and the frequency of their occurrence in the speech clinics under her direction, a special study of the underlying causes, conditions, and remedial measures has been undertaken.

In addition to all of the cases of various types observed in the speech clinics at the Child Guidance Clinic of Los Angeles and Pasadena, in the Orthopaedic Hospital Speech Clinic, and as private cases, our study included the analysis of material gathered in three nursery schools and represented one hundred children in these preschool groups. Two of the nursery schools included were those in which speech surveys and follow-up work were made on groups representing all five of the occupational levels mentioned in Barr's Occupational Rating Scale. They were: the Parents' Co-operative Nursery School, representing largely children from Groups I and II (of parents from the professional and semiprofessional or managerial, executive groups); and the Hollywood Day Nursery School, representing chiefly children of working mothers, from Occupational Groups III, IV, or V, namely, the skilled-, the semiskilled-, and the unskilled-labor groups. In the last group the fathers were in some cases unemployed or deceased. The groups in these schools contained normal or control speech cases and speech-defect groups.

The third group was composed entirely of children having speech defects, who had been referred to a special school of speech correction, namely, the Hill-Young School of Speech of Los Angeles. It represented children having defects of speech other than stuttering, and is therefore composed chiefly of: children with delayed speech, inhibited speech reactions, dyslalia, baby talk, and infantile perseverance in speech habits, and some children who had been variously diagnosed as retarded by reason of speech deprivation, aphasia, amnesia, aphemia, birth-injury, or encephalitis with a sufficiently good prognosis to make them eligible to the school; children with deferred mental diagnoses because of the special defects in speech, reading, and spelling which had made them ineligible for the ordinary training of the first grade in the public schools; and nursery-school children who had failed to profit by socialization of the usual type received in such schools, but with no other difficulty than a speech defect.

The first step was to determine something of the relative importance of our preconceived notions as to the causes of delayed speech in childhood as found in these various groups and to compare them with a normal-speech or control group. It is generally assumed, when a child fails to develop speech at the age when most children begin to talk and within a fairly wide range, chronologically, that he may be mentally deficient, decidedly retarded, or extremely deaf. Birth-injury, retardation due to postencephalitic condition, recurrent epileptiform seizures, convulsions, traumatic shock, and severe injury are said in medical reports to account for many of the failures of development in speech. However, a good many children presenting a good heredity and a clear history of normal birth, freedom from postnatal traumatic shock, accident, and unusual effects from childhood disease nevertheless are delayed in speech development but respond to individual training and to special speech-development methods. It is therefore safe to assume that in these cases there can be no actual lesion in the cortical or subcortical areas for speech reception and transmission, but that we are dealing rather with a complicated developmental factor, or a special type of retardation, due: (1) to failures in the child's perceptual development, the functioning of his sensory-receptive areas for speech, whether visual or auditory or both, and the transmission of speech impulses over his conduction mechanism to the motor areas of his brain; or (2) to the lack of formation of the various types of association necessary to the comprehension of meanings and the reception, retention, and reproduction of speech memories so as to convey them over the motor speech channels to the external speech mechanism.

If it can be shown by subsequent investigations that we are dealing with a special defect or arrest of development in which there is often no actual lesion and that there exists rather a type of developmental delay or special retardation in which the ordinary educational methods fail to arouse the accustomed responses, then we may hope to offer something in the nature of a satisfactory explanation for the many cases of arrested development which make surprising educational progress in the acquisition of speech and of ability in reading, spelling, and writing under individual and special instruction. The work of Gates at Columbia and of Fernald at the University of California at Los Angeles has indicated the efficacy of special methods and the need for new types of reading material suitable to the child who develops slowly.[6] Marion Monroe, as a result of her studies in the Chicago Institute of Juvenile Research,[7] developed diagnostic material useful for the detection of special defects in reading, writing, spelling, natural-handedness, mirror writing, and tendencies

[6] A. Gates, *Round the World Reader* (Yonkers, New York: World Book Co., 1930).

[7] Marion Monroe, *Children Who Cannot Read* (Chicago: University of Chicago Press, 1932); also *Diagnostic Reading Examination* (Chicago: C. H. Stoelting Co., 1932).

toward reversals of letters and digits, which account for a good deal of reading difficulty among left-handed children. Other useful diagnostic material is found in *Ayres Spelling Scale* for the detection of difficulties in spelling,[8] Durrell's *Tests for Oral and Silent Reading*,[9] Gray's *Tests of Oral Reading* for the testing and analysis of reading at various grade levels,[10] and the author's speech-testing material for detection and analysis of various difficulties and defects in speech.[11]

The general order in our research was as follows:

1. Analysis of the physical examination records for all children in the Hill-Young School of Speech, including an entire speech-corrective group.

2. Analysis of records of intelligence tests given to all children in the three nursery schools studied, including both corrective and control groups.

3. Analysis of speech tests given to all children in the three nursery schools, both corrective and control groups.

4. Analysis of audiometer test reports given to the children in residence in the Hill-Young School and to an equal number in the two outside nursery schools.

5. The making of a silent film to aid in studying the child's reaction during speech training and to show methods of securing responses from children with delayed speech.

Let us now consider the results of each of these studies in turn.

REPORTS OF PHYSICAL EXAMINATIONS[12]

The histories of twenty-three children who were pupils in the Hill-Young School within a twenty-two-month period, averaging about fifteen children per year, were included. The group included all children received within that period with the exception of a few children who were in the school too short a time.

In the histories of the entire group we find no particularly significant factor or group of factors which might represent an etiology of speech defects in young children. Among unfavorable "habits" and physical conditions we find listed in about equal proportion the following: finicky food habits, constipation, abnormal appetite, frequent colds, indigestion, sleeplessness, and enuresis.

Injury at birth is a possible factor in a few cases, underweight at birth being also reported in several cases. Several tonsillectomies had been per-

[8] *Ayres Spelling Scale* (Russell Sage Foundation, 1915).

[9] D. D. Durrell, *Analysis of Reading Difficulty* (Yonkers, New York: World Book Co., 1937).

[10] W. S. Gray, *Diagnostic Reading Tests* (Chicago: C. H. Stoelting Co., 1933).

[11] *Blanton-Stinchfield Speech Tests and Measurements* (Chicago: C. H. Stoelting Co., 1923, 1937).

[12] For help in assembling and compiling the following statistical report the writers wish to acknowledge their indebtedness to Dr. Hugh K. Berkeley, pediatrician, and Dr. Charles Lyle Hawk, orthopedist, attending physicians at the special school.

formed either before or after entering the school, and adenoidectomies had been performed in a few cases. There were some cases of glandular disorder and three cases of postoperative cleft-palate speech; and the history of past illnesses and childhood diseases indicated that more children had had measles, whooping cough, mumps, croup, and rheumatism than other types of illnesses. Thirty percent of the cases were entirely negative on the side of childhood diseases or past illnesses. It is possible, of course, that the histories were incomplete; but each had been made out by the physician most recently in charge of the child, and in all cases the histories had been made out at the request of the school by the physician in charge of the child at home, or by a physician of the parent's selection, at the time when he entered the school.

MENTAL TESTS

Because of reports of backwardness in some of these children a study was made to determine the mental status of the entire group in the Hill-Young School over a three-year period, as well as for the speech-corrective and the control groups in the two outside nursery schools, in a single year. There were some indications, according to psychological records available, that mental deficiency might be one of the chief etiological factors in producing speech defects. Tables I and II indicate the results of our study.

TABLE I

SUMMARY OF INTELLIGENCE TESTS GIVEN AT THE HILL-YOUNG SCHOOL OF SPEECH, COVERING A THREE-YEAR PERIOD

Name of Test	Chrono-logical Age, Months	Range	Mental Age, Months	Range	IQ	Range	No. of Cases
	Median Scores and Ranges						
Binet-Terman	66–69	31–136	66	22–108	91–94	50–131	44
Kuhlman	57	31–113	51	21.6–82.5	86.5	45–125	22
Goodenough Drawing	71–79	44–117	78–81	36*–131	97.5	46*–147	16
Seguin Form Board (Merrill-Palmer)	72	59–720 secs.	(Median Time Score, 110 secs.; or 85th decile for 4½ years)†				15

* Or below.

† Above average for highest norm given, at 4½ years.

From Table I it may be seen that the Binet (Stanford Revision) and the Kuhlman tests were used, both being standardized tests, and it being necessary to begin to test below the three-year level with younger children. Also it was thought advisable at the outset to test with both series on some of the same children, to allow for differences between the tests. On twenty-two cases the Kuhlman tests were given, and on forty-four cases the Stanford-Binet. It was found that so slight a difference existed between the test results on the children to whom both were given that the performance tests were then introduced and sixteen of the younger children were tested on the Goodenough Drawing Test and fifteen on the Seguin Form Board from the Merrill-Palmer Series. It is interesting to note that on the performance tests our children did considerably better than on the Binet or the Kuhlman test. Dealing with concrete materials rather than with abstractions favors these children, apparently, and is a further indication of their moto-kinesthetic tendencies, as contrasted with ideation depending more largely upon use of language, verbalization, and auditory and visual cues. For this reason the moto-kinesthetic training outlined in Part I of this volume would seem to be more logical and effective educationally than training dependent upon auditory and visual perception primarily.

We wished to ascertain to what extent the language handicap entered into the intelligence rating and what the effect of later training might be. On the Binet tests the mental-age median was less than three months lower than the chronological age with this group. On the Kuhlman tests the mental age averaged six months lower than the chronological age. This shows the average retardation to be not over six months on either test. On the performance tests the mental rating was considerably higher, the median intelligence quotient being 97.5 on the Goodenough Drawing Test given to sixteen children. The Seguin Form Board yielded a median above the average for $4\frac{1}{2}$ years, which is as high as the norms go on this test. Obviously, many of these children are motor- rather than visuo-auditory in their thinking and in their activities.

Children with such mental ratings cannot be considered dull-normal nor sufficiently retarded even in the Kuhlman performance, which penalizes them rather more than the Binet, to be assigned to special or opportunity classes in the public schools, as the retardation does not average two or more years. We must therefore assume that mental deficiency is not the primary factor in causing the delayed or backward speech development in these cases. That they need special speech training, however, in order to make normal progress in school, will be evident, we believe, from a further consideration of these data.

In Table II, r equals the Pearson coefficient of correlation, computed directly for the Stanford-Binet group, and for the other tests obtained indirectly by converting ρ (calculated by the Rank-Difference Method) into r (see Garrett, *Statistics in Psychology and Education*, Table XX, p. 192).

SUMMARY OF MENTAL TESTS

1. There is a positive, statistically significant correlation between speech score and M.A. as measured by the Stanford-Binet, the Kuhlman-

TABLE II

CORRELATIONS OF SPEECH SCORE WITH MENTAL AGE AND
CHRONOLOGICAL AGE

Name of Test	Speech and M.A.			Speech and C.A.			No. of Cases
	r	P.E.	*r*/P.E.	*r*	P.E.	*r*/P.E.	
Stanford-Binet	.443	.082	5.4	.183	.096	1.9	44
Kuhlman-Binet	.41	.125	3.3	.06	.15	0.4	22
Goodenough Drawing .	.61	.11	5.5	.16	.17	0.9	16
Seguin Form Board*..	.525	.132	3.9	.467	.143	3.3	15

* Time score instead of mental age.

Binet, and the Goodenough Drawing Scale. There is also the same type of correlation between speech score and the time score on the Seguin Form Board.

2. The correlation between speech score and mental age cannot be due to the chronological age factor, inasmuch as the coefficients of correlation between speech score and C.A. for the Stanford-Binet, the Kuhlman-Binet, and the Goodenough groups are low, and statistically insignificant.

3. There is a positive, significant correlation between speech score and chronological age in the Seguin group. Whether or not this correlation is accidental, it prevents us from attributing significance to the correlation between speech score and the Seguin mental age.

The findings suggest the following interpretations of the data : First, the speech tests and the intelligence tests used both test language functions. The lowered IQ may be in that case due to speech difficulty. However, children with the highest speech score have the highest score also in Goodenough Drawing, and those with lowest speech scores have lowest Goodenough scores; and therefore Goodenough does not depend on the ability to speak (note Goodenough correlation, column *r*, of .61). Second, speech involves functions which are basic to, although not directly measured by, the intelligence tests. Normal speech therefore depends upon intelligence. Speech, according to our data, is somewhat more closely related to performance tests than to those involving language. One assumes that there should be a higher correlation between speech and Binet tests than between speech and performance tests, but we find a slightly higher correlation between speech and performance tests on our cases.

The question immediately arises as to whether or not speech training affects the mental age and whether it can be expected to raise the intelligence quotient. These data possibly have some implications for the method of speech training with young children. On the basis of the results found, it would be interesting to test by further research the motor approach, dealing with concrete materials in speech correction, in comparison with methods dealing with abstractions and with auditory imagery primarily. At present education favors the abstract, auditory (and visual) appeal, except in some special systems or institutions dealing with severly handicapped children. Our findings further indicate that there is more virtue in the moto-kinesthetic approach to speech development in children with delayed or backward speech, in cases of deafness, childhood illnesses, and the like, than in the commonly employed methods stressing language acquisition mostly through auditory and visual channels.

For purposes of comparison of the speech cases in the special school (the Hill-Young School of Speech) with other nursery-school groups among whom speech defects were not a special problem to a recognized extent, data (Table III) were compiled from children at the Parents' Co-operative Nursery School of Los Angeles and the Assistance League Day Nursery of Hollywood.

TABLE III

SPEECH- AND INTELLIGENCE-TEST SHOWING OF TWO GROUPS OF
NON-PROBLEM CHILDREN

School and Test	Chronological Age, Months		Intelligence Quotient		No. of Cases
	Normal Speech Group	Corrective Group	Normal Speech Group	Corrective Group	
Parents' Co-operative Nursery School					
Stanford-Binet	57	43	128	120	48
Assistance League Day Nursery					
Merrill-Palmer	47	48	103–5	104	21

It is important to note that in the Parents' Co-operative Nursery School group children in the speech-corrective group averaged over a year younger than those in the normal-speech group. As the parents of these children were of superior economic and social status, it is probable that the presence of a speech defect or slow development in their children caused them to place them in nursery school at an earlier age than they might otherwise have done, in order that socialization and special training might help to develop them and to improve the speech function. In the Assistance League Day Nursery group, for children of working mothers, there was practically no difference in the average ages found for the corrective and for the control group. While the IQ averaged higher among children in the private nursery school than among those in the free nursery school, all of the children, correctives and speech cases, in the Parents' Co-operative School group earned IQ's which distinguished them as above average. The IQ's were about equal in both groups for the second nursery school, the Assistance League or close to 100 in both cases. There is thus seen to be no retardation in intelligence, according to these averages for both schools, in either the corrective or the control groups.

One of the startling and interesting facts which has come out of our study is the discovery of changes which have occurred in intelligence levels following special training and improved conditions. Having been for many years devotees of the theory of the relative constancy of the IQ, it was with some surprise that the writers discovered that under favorable conditions not only was it possible to improve children to whom an IQ could not fairly be assigned, before training, but that in several cases where children had been originally diagnosed as feeble-minded or dull-normal the intelligence changed not only a few points but in some cases many points and there was a decided improvement in the child's entire perceptual level and adaptation to environment, indicating an advance in intelligence. That this was actually the case was evident from the change obtained in scores on mental tests after a period of training ranging from six months to two years in several children in different nursery schools or clinical groups studied.

A little girl from a superior environment, originally diagnosed as of doubtful mentality and possibly mentally deficient, was found to have an IQ of 100, after a year's training in the special school. A second case was that of a boy rejected by the public schools as a nonreader and with an IQ of 57 on his original mental test at the age of 8 years 2 months. He had been delayed in entering school because of delayed speech development and when he entered school was diagnosed as feeble-minded. A retest after a year's training in the special school gave him an IQ of 80 on the Stanford-Binet Scale and one of 73 on the Kuhlman tests. Another child referred to the school for delayed speech and diagnosed as feeble-minded received an IQ of 70 at the time of her mental test on the Stanford-Binet Scale and an M.A. of better than 4 years on performance tests; her chronological age at that time was 4 years 3 months.[13]

Another child, who did not talk at the time when he entered the school at the age of 3 years 11 months, was then given a tentative IQ of 54 on the Stanford-Binet Scale. When tested a year later he earned an IQ of 88 in the Kuhlman tests and one of 89 on the Stanford-Binet. He had mastered language and expression so that he used sentences of several words, intelligible speech, with scarcely any remaining letter substitutions or inaccuracies in words in common usage and of his own experiential level.

A boy who entered the school at the age of two years, with a history of delayed speech, unintelligible jargon, and possible feeble-mindedness

---

[13] S. T. Orton, *Development of Speech Understanding in Relation to Intelligence* (Langhorne, Pa.: Child Research Clinic, Woods Schools, Vol. I, No. 6, 1936).

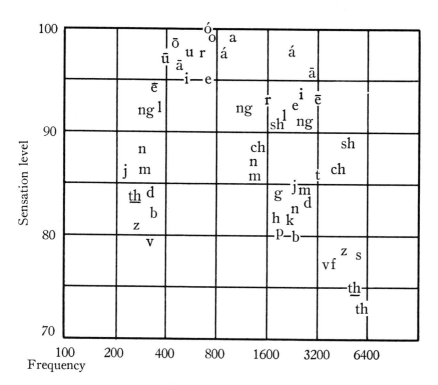

Fig. 1.—Fletcher's diagram.

Fig. 2.—Speech lesson. Toys from the treasure box represent all of the English sounds.

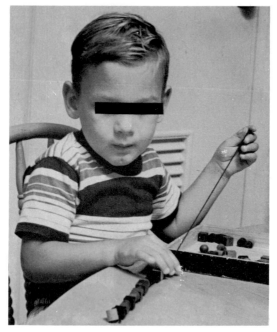

Fig. 3.—Finer hand and finger co-or-
dinations, taught through stringing beads.
(Courtesy: Nursery School for the Visually
Handicapped, Los Angeles, California.)

Fig. 4.—Activity on the jungle gym for muscular co-ordination. (Courtesy: Nursery School
for the Visually Handicapped, Los Angeles,
California.)

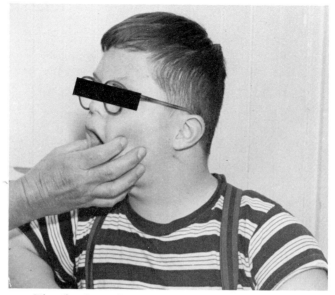

Fig. 5.—Learning to give the correct *aw* sound in "ball." (Courtesy: The Cedars School, Ross, California.)

Fig. 6.—Sound and syllable matching in reading and speech. (Note: In working with backward children, it is often necessary to return to first principles, and to acquaint the child with phonetic sounds and syllables, in order that he may identify and recognize those sounds in words. (Courtesy: The Cedars School, Ross, California.)

Fig. 7.—Word and picture matching in reading. (Courtesy: The Cedars School, Ross, California.)

Fig. 8.—First lessons in writing. (Courtesy: The Cedars School, Ross, California.)

was retested at about three years of age, at which time he received a mental age rating of 3 years 10.5 months—an IQ of 125 on the Stanford-Binet Scale and one of 129 on the Kuhlman tests. The improvement in speech in this case was of special significance, as was shown in a very practical way. On being put to bed one night, he began to cry and insisted that his mother leave the door open and the window closed. As this was contrary to custom, the mother objected and asked the child for an explanation; the child replied, "Because I don't like that man that came in through the window last night, and came over here and stood by my bed." On investigation the mother found that the screen had been torn away from the window and that heavy footprints were visible in the soil outside; it was evident that during the previous evening, while the family were entertaining visitors in an adjoining room, someone had entered the child's room and had then hastily departed. What might have been the possible effect of an experience like this upon the plastic mind of the child had he been unable to give expression to his fear, and had the mother insisted upon following the usual procedure, it is not difficult to guess.

To test the validity of our belief that speech training had been influential in producing an improved mental status we retested several children in the Hill-Young School of Speech. Some of these children at the time when they entered the school had presented histories of extreme backwardness, delayed speech, unintelligible speech, maladjustment, stuttering, and school failure. Some had been rated as of average intelligence, some had received an indeterminate intelligence quotient, and some had been rated retarded or possibly mentally deficient. In all of these cases described not only was there great improvement in personality and general adjustment but there was increased comprehension and power of communication and of understanding which were indicated by the higher IQ's. In some cases the change was slight. In others the improvement was considerable, and in many cases it was surprisingly high, as compared with the first rating obtained.

SUMMARY

1. Many cases of delayed speech in which causes were obscure have been classified as aphasics in the past.

2. Literature on special disabilities is comparatively recent.

3. Remedial measures for disabilities in reading, writing, spelling, and speech defects are now extensively employed.

4. In many places the application of such remedial measures is confined to university laboratories and hospital and child-guidance clinics.

5. More progressive school systems provide special training for specially handicapped children, through development or adjustment rooms, and special classes.

6. Our study includes the analysis of physical examination records, mental tests, audiometer tests, performance tests, and speech tests.

7. No single etiological factor or syndrome stands out as the chief cause for the existence of delayed speech and speech defects.

8. Mental tests indicate that these children, while retarded slightly in rate of progress at the onset of speech training, progress rapidly and actually improve in perceptual ability, as is shown by changes in the IQ's in many instances.

9. In addition to the various forms of training previously noted, our own experience with the direct stimulation of the muscles of speech, as shown in the moto-kinesthetic method, in the earlier years of childhood, brings a more definite development and correction of speech than has been possible otherwise. The early learning tends to associate the idea with the correct movements, as well as with the auditory and visual patterns.

CHAPTER SEVENTEEN

MEASUREMENTS: SPEECH TESTS

Observations on the speech of children just learning to talk yield much valuable information to the intelligent observer. Many parents who are ordinarily sensitive to differences in dialects and pronunciation and to differences in forms of expression and social customs associated with persons in various walks of life are often surprisingly indifferent to, or unaware of, marked deviations from good speech in members of their own households.

As a part of our experimental study, speech tests were given to all children in three nursery-school groups. The same tests were given also to all children referred to the speech clinic of the Child Guidance Clinic of Los Angeles and Pasadena and to the Orthopaedic Hospital speech clinic. All together they represent a study of one hundred and thirteen nursery-school children and about seventy clinical cases.

With children of from three-and-a-half to five years we used picture tests which contained all the sounds of English, using the consonants in initial, middle, and final positions in test words, and employing all the vowels and diphthongs and some blends, such as *fr, tr, bl, tl*. The test included one hundred sounds in all, and was graded on a scale of 100. For greater usefulness with younger children who are easily distracted on the longer test, and for whom it is essential to determine only whether or not they are able to produce the desired sound at all, regardless of position in the word, a shorter and simpler test was employed—an object test. This consisted of objects representing all the consonant sounds of English and the vowels, the entire test being scored on a basis of 180 points. There were forty-eight sounds in all, but the more difficult sounds were weighted more heavily than the easy sounds. The simpler sounds were graded 1, 2, or 3 for "poor," "average," or "excellent" articulation, the more difficult sounds being counted as 2, 4, or 6, for "poor," "average," or "excellent." Zero was assigned when no speech sound was obtained. When the numerical values were added, the total score might range from 0 (no speech) to 180 points.

The speech tests used were the standardized *Blanton-Stinchfield Speech Tests and Measurements*[1] which include articulation tests arranged by the author.[2]

Table IV shows the principal types of errors found among one hundred children of the three nursery schools.

---

[1] Published by C. H. Stoelting Co. (Chicago, 1926), and Kentucky Press for the Blind (Louisville, Ky., 1926).

[2] Sara Stinchfield, *Speech Disorders* (New York: Harcourt, Brace & Co., 1933).

TABLE IV

SUMMARY OF PRINCIPAL TYPES OF SPEECH ERRORS FOUND IN THREE NURSERY-
SCHOOL GROUPS (100 CASES), ARRANGED IN ORDER OF FREQUENCY*

Order of Occur- rence	Hill-Young School of Speech (31 cases)	Parents' Co-operative Nursery School (48 cases)	Assistance League Day Nursery School (21 cases)
1.	*th* (voiced and voiceless)	*th* (voiced and voiceless)	*th* (voiced and voiceless)
2.	*s* and *z* sounds	*s* and *z* sounds	*s* and *z* sounds
3.	*l* and *r* in all words and combinations	*sh* and *zh* sounds	*zh* and *sh* sounds
4.	*sh* and *zh* sounds	*l* and *r* sounds	*l* and *r* sounds
5.	*ch* and *j* sounds	....	*v* sounds†
Percentage showing speech de- fects	100	29	40‡

* Minor errors not included.
† Several children of foreign parentage.
‡ Boys only; no girls listed for speech defects in this school.

ERROR FREQUENCIES

In the special school of speech we found that sixteen times as many errors were made by boys as by girls; we checked 429 errors against boys, as compared with 26 against girls. As girls are in a ratio of 1 to 5 as compared with the boys in this school, we should expect the boys to register more errors than the girls, because they outnumber them; but the actual percentage of errors among the boys is quite out of proportion to their ratio as compared with girls in the school. Several children had no speech at all on entering school, aside from unintelligible babbling or jargon. All were required to make some improvement in speech after a reasonable trial or they were dropped from the school, so that these children represent a fair sampling of the children usually in attendance.

The range of scores was from 0 to 171, out of a possible score of 180 points. The median score was between 114 and 128 points.

At the Parents' Co-operative Nursery School the children represented the type usually found in the standard nursery school. In this school 125 errors were recorded for girls, as against 139 by boys—a ratio of 9 to 10— out of a total of forty-eight children tested.

Boys were in the majority here, as in the other school, but in smaller proportion. This is important, as it is estimated that boys in general are slower in speech development and have more speech difficulty and speech defects than girls. Most of the children in this school represented Groups I and II (professional and semiprofessional or managerial) on Barr's Occupational Rating Scale. Of all children tested, 29 percent were designated as in need of remedial speech training for difficulties ranging from minor inaccuracies and frequent letter substitutions to delayed speech, absence of articulate speech, and mild stuttering.

In the Assistance League Day Nursery School, where children of working mothers are given nursery-school training and care during the day, there were 138 errors made by boys and 25 by girls. The error ratio here was 5 to 1, the errors made by the boys far outnumbering the proportion of boys to girls in this school. Of the eight cases referred for remedial speech work, following the survey, all were boys. Three children in this group had only a few vocalizations, mostly in the nature of unintelligible babbling but containing numerous consonant and vowel sounds; and in each case the age was over two-and-a-half years.

In the Parents' Co-operative School the median score for all children tested was $167\frac{1}{2}$ out of a possible 180 points. For the speech cases it was between 90 and 114. The range of scores in this school was from 0 to 180, representing the widest possible range. The lack of speech and the realization of the possibility of educational retardation through speech deprivation had undoubtedly influenced the parents in placing these children in the school. Socialization and education, however, had not at the time of testing enabled these children to talk plainly enough to be understood by teachers and other children.

In the Assistance League Day Nursery School the median score for girls tested was 114 out of a possible 180 points. For boys it was 137, or slightly higher than for girls. This closely parallels the average scores for boys and girls in the special school of speech. The range of scores was from 50 to 179 out of a possible 180 points, allowing credit, according to the scale of values given in the speech test, for the vowels and consonants which occurred in the babbling or otherwise inarticulate speech of these children. There were no children who were entirely negative to speech stimuli or unable to produce any speech sounds. The occupational backgrounds in this school represented mostly Groups III and IV on Barr's Occupational Rating Scale (the skilled-labor and semiskilled-labor groups).

Among the boys were found frequent omissions of final consonants, letter substitutions such as *t* or *d* for *th*, difficulty with *s* and *z* sounds, difficulty with *sh* and *zh*, *ch* and *j*, and any combinations or blends containing these sounds. Echolalia was present in some cases. Speech substitutions were much rarer among the girls. Occasional hesitancy due to shyness and insecurity was noticeable. As this is sometimes an early indication of tendencies leading to stuttering, it is best to increase the child's self-confidence and build up habits of immediate and ready responses in speech situations at as early an age as possible, in order to prevent possible stuttering. Difficulty on *f*, *y*, and *th* sounds seemed to occur more often than any other type of letter substitutions among the little girls.

In the most conspicuous case of speech defect in this school, that of a boy with echolalia tendencies, whose spontaneous speech consisted only of babbling, unintelligible sounds, or those intermingled with vowel and consonant sounds in a sort of inarticulate jargon, we found a low IQ on the initial speech test, by reason of retardation by deprivation. The medical history was negative. The child had been reared apart from other children, in an environment unfavorable to a small child, and almost entirely isolated during the mother's working hours. At the age of three years, on entering nursery school, his speech was as described above. On retesting, some four and a half months after he entered the nursery school, and after remedial speech and educational methods had been applied, his intelligence quotient showed a marked and surprising advance, equal to the status of the dull-normal, and definitely removing him from the moron classification. His speech development represented a decided advance over the early echolalia and babbling. It was after the application of the moto-kinesthetic measures that his rapid advance began. The ordinary nursery-school progress seemed too slow to obtain the desired speech progress in such a case.[3]

His speech test after four and a half months revealed certain difficulties, but the speech level as a whole advanced from the early stages of echolalia, babbling, and unintelligibility to entirely intelligible speech, characterized by some letter substitutions and omissions.

TYPES OF ERRORS

As to the types of errors found when the speech tests were given to all children in the three nursery-school groups, Table V indicates many points of similarity among the three groups, although the rank order varies slightly for different sounds giving difficulty in the three groups.

Greater difficulty was observed on sounds in initial and final positions than in mid-position in the words given. It was possible to check for the consonants in all positions by using a picture test for this purpose. The picture test was therefore used in addition to the object test, as it contained pictures in which the speech stimulus was a word in which the consonant occurred first in initial, then in mid- and in final position. This test also contained all the vowels in the English language and had been previously standardized.[4] From a phonetic standpoint it is true that the position of a consonant affects its relative strength or influence in a word, as mid-position apparently tends to lessen the effect of a slight inaccuracy, even to the extent of sometimes obscuring the defect entirely, unless the tone is considerably amplified. The frequencies given in these tables include the number of times in which the sound was given inaccurately in all three positions, initial, middle, and final.

It is important to try to determine to what extent auditory acuity and perception enter into the matter of speech accuracy and speech develop-

---

[3] J. M. Nielsen, *Agnosia, Apraxia, Aphasia* (Los Angeles : Neurological Society of Los Angeles, 1936), p. 195.

[4] *Blanton-Stinchfield Speech Tests and Measurements.*

TABLE V

SUMMARY OF SPEECH INACCURACIES FOUND IN THREE NURSERY-SCHOOL
GROUPS (100 CASES), ARRANGED IN ORDER OF FREQUENCY*

Order of Occurrence	Hill-Young School of Speech (31 cases)	Parents' Co-operative School (48 cases)	Assistance League Day Nursery School (21 cases)
1. . . . . *th* (voiced and voiceless)	*th* sounds	*s* and *z*
2. . . . . *s* and *z*	*s* and *z*	*th* sounds
3. . . . . *l* and combinations	*l* and combinations	*sh* and *zh*
4. . . . . *sh* and *zh*	*f* and *v*	*l* and combinations
5. . . . . *k, g,* and *ng* sounds	*sh, zh, ch,* and *j*	*ch* and *j*
6. . . . . *ch* and *j*	*y* and *w*	*r* and combinations
7. . . . . *f* and *v*	*r* and combinations	*y* sounds
8. . . . . *r* and combinations	*k, g,* and *ng* sounds	*-air* (vowel glide)
9. . . . . *y* sounds	*aw* (vowel sound)	*-ire* (vowel glide)
10. . . . . *w* sounds	*-air*	*a* as in "arm"
11. . . . . *-ir,* and *-ear*	*-er, ir* as in 'burr"	*o* as in "go"
12. . . . . *-air, -ire, -ower*	*oo* as in "boot"	. . . .†
13. . . . . *-aw* as in "saw"	. . . .†	. . . .†

* Minor errors not included.
† No other sounds stood out as particularly difficult, at this point in the test, for these two groups.

ment. Since neither the physical nor the mental examinations, nor the speech tests, had enabled us to isolate any single factor or group of factors which might be considered the chief causes of the speech impairment, it was important to discover whether or not auditory inacuity or defective auditory perception was present to an appreciable extent in these cases.

We had observed that many of the children who failed to profit by the ordinary environment in home and nursery school, so far as speech progress was concerned, made rapid progress when given "special handling" in the form of speech training in a setting adapted to verbalization and socialization. It was also noted that numerous cases of children who had originally been diagnosed as mentally deficient showed a gain which was often very surprising when retested. In some cases this amounted to twenty percent or more improvement or advance in IQ. This seemed to indicate that there was a mental and emotional release which came with speech development and communication, and that something was happening to the intellectual life of the child which resulted in actually improved perceptions. We felt that this offered a new angle to the entire problem of speech correction, inasmuch as we have formerly been inclined to accept the probability of the constancy of the IQ without much question. While constancy of the IQ seems to hold for normal children who progress at the average rate of development, there seems to be some doubt as to its constancy in cases of delayed development, special handicap, retardation, or slow development due to any of a number of deviations in the physical or mental growth of some children.

Audiometer tests were given to all children then in residence in the Hill-Young School of Speech and to two equated groups in outside nursery schools. The audiometer used was the Jones-Knudsen instrument in the Acoustical Laboratory of the University of California at Los Angeles. The tests were given by one of the authors of this book. Several children were retested by a technician for the Western Electric 2A Audiometer, in order to recheck our results on several cases with another type of instrument. The records obtained were closely parallel. The number of children tested was too small to allow for sweeping conclusions, but there were twelve children from the special school and an equal number, six each, chosen from the two outside nursery schools who were tested because they were speech-defect cases and had been assigned to speech-correction groups. Also several children with normal speech were chosen from the two outside schools to serve as a control or "normal speech" group. We had expected to find in our corrective groups a drop in the curve for auditory acuity at one end of the scale or the other; that is, for low tones of around 64 to 128 cycles per second there should be a drop in the curve for cases of conduction deafness, or at the upper end of the scale, for frequencies of around 4,000 to 8,000 cycles per second, there should be a drop in the curve in cases of perceptive deafness. We found, rather, a general reduction in auditory acuity for the entire range of sounds amounting to about 30 percent.[5] This seemed to indicate that there was neither exclusively perceptive nor conductive impairment and no complete loss of hearing for either high or low tones, but that the intensity of the stimulus had to be increased by about twenty to thirty decibels for tones within the speech range, in order to elicit a dependable response from the child.

Where we find a reduction in auditory acuity amounting to 30 percent or more, we recommend training a child to respond to speech stimuli by educating him along lines to which he can best respond, namely, through visual, motor, and kinesthetic avenues. Speech therapy, in such cases, should make use of the kinesthetic method in order to arouse to greater activity the dormant or defective cerebral impressions. Amplification devices also speed the development of normal speech in such cases.

DEAFNESS AND AUDITORY INACUITY

A child who is congenitally deaf, or one who suffers from acquired deafness, either develops no articulate speech without training, or possesses defects in speech due to inability to hear speech sounds with normal acuity. Such children acquire inaccurate speech movements and produce letter substitutions or mutations which stand out as imperfections or defects of utterance because of their phonetic inaccuracy. Not hearing speech

[5] A. W. and E. R. Ewing, *The Handicap of Deafness* (New York: Longmans, Green & Co., Inc., 1938).

sounds, the deaf child lacks the autocritical power of sound-analysis and self-correction which the ordinary child possesses. Children who are born deaf or who acquire deafness during the early years of childhood, before speech habits have become well established, are usually educated in institutions for the deaf or in special classes for the hard-of-hearing in the public schools. In cases where the hearing loss is slight or scarcely noticeable, it often remains unsuspected by parents and teachers for months or even years. Therefore, accurate audiometer tests should be made at frequent intervals in all schools.

Few of us realize the importance of normal hearing for speech development, and there are many children who are by no means deaf-mutes who nevertheless have reduced auditory acuity or poor auditory perceptions. They become educationally retarded unless the handicap is recognized during the early years and special measures are undertaken to counteract the effects of the hearing deficiency. There is a close relationship between defects of auditory perception, "congenital word-deafness," "word-blindness," poor spelling, and dyslexia, with its various reading and writing disabilities. In speech training, as with the deaf-mute, we should utilize to a much greater extent visual, motor, and kinesthetic impressions, building up clearer perceptions, strengthening the weak auditory perceptions, and gradually weaving together the strands which form the visual, auditory, motor, and kinesthetic memories for speech sounds, since there are undoubtedly children who do not respond readily to auditory stimuli. When we combine the kinesthetic with the ordinary visual and auditory avenues of learning by means of which most children learn to talk, we are strengthening the impressions already received and increasing the child's chances of understanding and perceiving meanings which lead to overt expression in speech. The cerebral impressions aroused through kinesthesia and sense of muscle movement help to combine visual with other impressions, and may even arouse the dormant auditory sensory and perceptive areas to functional activity.

Speech frequencies include sounds ranging from about 125 to about 6,500 cycles per second; but for ordinary purposes the sounds ranging from about 512 to about 4,000 cycles are the most significant, as these are the tones which we hear most frequently in human speech. Sounds of high frequencies, such as we find in *s*, *z*, and voiceless *th*, are very difficult to hear whenever perceptive or nerve deafness exists. Sounds below 500 cycles per second are difficult to hear in conductive deafness, in which the lower frequencies are eliminated. The vowels consist of simpler tones than those of the consonants. Even when there is less intensity of tone, we can usually hear the vowels more easily than the consonants.

Deaf persons, failing to hear speech sounds adequately, tend to develop a "deaf" voice, which is characterized by considerable monotony and lack of resonance. Voiceless sounds (the consonants such as *f*, *p*, *t*, *k*, *sh*, *ch*) may be easily omitted by them from the ends or beginnings of words, or they may be mutilated or changed by the deaf person who has never heard them correctly nor learned how to say them. Children who are deaf to the higher frequencies often substitute the sound of *th* or *sh* for *s*. Instead of saying "see," they say something which sounds more like "thee" (voiceless *th*) or "shee." In a word like "fish," they may say "fis," or "fith," and yet not be able to recognize the difference between their own speech sounds and the correct ones as given by the teacher. We find that this is true of adults who are deaf to the higher frequencies and who may have lisped from early childhood and yet never have been referred to a speech clinic or a speech teacher for correction. Sometimes the defect is noticed for the first time when the speaker attempts to make a phonographic record of his speech or when he speaks through the microphone. He may then be debarred from recording or from lecturing because of the way in which the instrument intensifies his relatively mild speech inaccuracy.

After the patient has been examined and his type of deafness determined, he should be further tested to find out what kind of amplification is best suited to his needs. By using the most suitable type for his individual case, the teacher will at once promote improvement in understanding and will greatly enhance the possibility of speech improvement. The use of some amplification in dealing with children with minor defects of hearing, as well as for the inattentive, nonverbal, or delayed-speech types, is to be very strongly recommended to the teacher of speech. Much further experimentation with various types of audio-amplifiers would be of material assistance to the teacher and to the mother of the deaf child. It is certain that the newer types of audio-amplification will prove of the greatest assistance to the speech correctionist, in speech clinical work.

Two definitions are needed at this point for the sake of clearness. The term "hard-of-hearing" we shall use to designate a person who has had normal hearing. By a "deaf" person we mean one who has always had defective auditory function or reduced hearing. Many children with delayed speech might be termed "deaf," even though they have residual hearing. Thus the hard-of-hearing person is one who has a partial loss of hearing, while the deaf is a person who has a severe loss of auditory function.

This leads us to what may well be the most significant part of our study of the etiology of speech defects in young children. Referring back to Table V (p. 147), we find that in two schools the errors which occurred most frequently were on voiced and voiceless *th* sounds (as in "thin" and "mother"). The sound-analysis charts compiled by Fletcher of the Bell Telephone Laboratories show us that the *th* sounds are of high characteristic frequency, and on Fletcher's diagram showing the characteristics of most of the fundamental speech sounds we find that *th* as in "thin" is the sound of the lowest intensity and the highest frequency of all

English speech sounds. The voiced *th,* as in "mother," has ten times as much power as the voiceless *th* in "thin." It consists of frequencies of between 3,200 and 6,400 cycles per second. Voiceless *th,* therefore, is a fainter sound, acoustically, than any of the other sounds of language.[6]

A study of our list of error-frequencies among children of the Assistance League Day Nursery School shows that *s* and *z* sounds caused the highest percentage of errors. On referring to the Fletcher Diagram again, we find that these sounds are of less intensity and higher characteristic frequencies than most of the other consonants. Their characteristic frequencies consist of around 3,200 to 6,400 vibrations, although *z* contains some tones which are much lower in pitch and louder than the high-frequency components.

In the other two nursery schools, both private, we find that *s* and *z* occupy second place among errors, while in the free nursery schools the *th* sounds appear in first place and the *s* and *z* appear as second in order of difficulty. Since the first two schools represent about three fourths of the children studied, it is possible that the *th* sounds are the ones which are most frequently incorrect, with *z* and *s* taking second place.

The sounds which occur in third position on the lists for the two private schools are *l* sounds and combinations containing this sound. This sound is in fourth position on the list for the free nursery school. This is classed as a semivowel in Crandall's tables.[7] From the standpoint of sensation level it is a fairly powerful sound, and occurs in speech with about the same frequency as the *th* sounds according to Fletcher.[8] While one of its characteristic frequencies is between 1,600 and 3,200 vibrations, it has others which increase its intensity and audibility. This should not be a difficult sound to hear, therefore, and it is possible that the explanation of its difficulty in speech is to be found in its "poor visibility." That is, it is not easy for a child to *see* it, in others, well enough to grasp quickly the idea of the movements involved in placing the tongue in position for the *l* sound, and many children confuse it with a lip movement, giving a *w* for an *l* sound in learning to talk (saying "wook" for "look"). The child does not get this by himself, but once it is directed by the teacher, the child is able to correct it almost immediately. Moreover, the tongue muscles must move with sufficient definiteness and tension to form the kind of resonance chamber necessary for the quality of tone which goes to make up the *l* sound, and children who speak with many oral inaccuracies and with lax, careless, indefinite muscle movements usually fail on the *l* sound when beginning to talk. It is one of the sounds which most children acquire with some difficulty, and therefore it is probably one of

[6] H. Fletcher, *Speech and Hearing* (New York: D. Van Nostrand Co., 1929), pp. 73, 74, 76.

[7] I. B. Crandall, *The Sounds of Speech,* tables taken from *Bell Telephone Laboratory Reprint B-162-1,* November 1925.

[8] H. Fletcher, *op. cit.,* pp. 84, 141.

the tones which present muscular difficulties. It is less easily seen than a lip movement, such as is used in making the *w* sound.

In the first or special school of speech, the sounds *sh* and *zh* occur fourth in rank among errors. In the Parents' Co-operative School, the *f* and *v* take fourth place, while in the Assistance League Day Nursery School, *sh* and *zh* occur in third position, and *ch* and *j* in fifth position. While *ch, j, sh,* and *zh* occur in fifth position in the Parents' Co-operative School, in the speech school *ch* and *j* appear in sixth position. Thus in all three schools these palatal sounds cause considerable difficulty for the child learning to talk. It is interesting to note that according to Fletcher most of these palatal sounds have high characteristic frequencies, although *j* and *zh*, voiced sounds, have some low characteristic frequencies which serve to increase their intensity. Since these sounds are in the region of 1,600 to 6,400 vibrations, they are more difficult to hear accurately than most of the consonants, and the child with deficient hearing often hears them imperfectly and reproduces them inaccurately. The fact that they are less easily distinguished by deaf children also indicates that they may be more difficult sounds for children with normal hearing, unless the auditory perceptions have been trained to distinguish minor differences in tonal qualities and to realize the importance of phonetic accuracy in reproduction, in order to distinguish between words and sounds of similar meaning.

The sounds of *k, g,* and *ng* cause more difficulty in the school of speech than in either of the other two schools. From the standpoint of auditory sensation, intensity, and frequency, these sounds differ little from the labials *b, p,* and *m*; but the muscle movement is very different in the former, and we believe that here, as on the *l* sound, the matter of visibility is one explanation for the frequent errors made. These sounds are made well back in the mouth—the back of the tongue making a contact with the uvula and an explosive movement occurring on voiceless *k* and the voiced *g*, but the position being maintained during the production of the nasal continuant *ng*. The greater intensity of the *ng* sound may explain the fact that it seems to be less difficult for children to acquire than the fainter *k* and *g* sounds.[9] Many children substitute a front-of-tongue *t* or *d* sound for the back-of-tongue *k* and *g* sound, saying "tat" for "cat" and "date" for "gate." Once they have become impressed by means of visual and kinesthetic cues as to the exact movements necessary for the production of these sounds, they soon acquire the correct habit.

The semivowels, *y* and *w*, cause some difficulty among children in two of the schools. Since these tones are fairly intense, in terms of sound levels,[10] although the *e* component in the *y* makes it relatively high-pitched as to fundamental tone, it seems to be partly a matter of lip-tension on the

[9] H. Fletcher, *op. cit.*, Fig. 44, reproduced here as Fig. 1.
[10] "Sound level" is the increase in intensity level above the threshold, and is measured in decibels.

w sounds, which causes it to give difficulty to lip-lazy, lethargic children, while the difficulty of seeing the direction of movement for the *y* sound, as well as its high-frequency components, considerable muscular tension, and high position of the tongue, make it probable that the difficulty is partly one of visibility, especially for children of poor visual imagery. A few trials at directing the line of movement and showing the child the accurate position are usually all that is necessary to enable him quickly to correct inaccuracies on the *w* and *y* sounds.

The *r* sound and all blends containing it present difficulty. This sound occurs in eighth position on the list of difficult sounds, in the speech school; in seventh position among errors in the second school; and in sixth position in the third school. Now *r* is a sound of good intensity, not at all difficult to hear, nor is it high in pitch, as it lies roughly between 500 and 1,600 vibrations on Fletcher's chart. Many children have great difficulty with both the *r* and the *l* sounds, and even though they may be able to make these sounds correctly, they often continue to substitute the lip movement of *w* during the attempted production of the *r* sound. The edges of the tongue should be flexible and free, and the tongue should move downward in the mouth during the production of *r*. It requires considerable muscle skill and agility. The child needs to be sufficiently eye-minded to be able to observe how adults produce this sound, in case it gives difficulty. We believe that in the case of *r* sounds, as well as in *l* sounds, the difficulty involves chiefly muscle skill and visual observation.

A few vowels present difficulties to some children, especially those calling for greater lip tension, such as *oo* in "boot," dipthongs like *ow* as in "cow" and *ou* as in "hour," glides such as *-ear*, *-ire*, and *-oor* in words like "ear," "fire" and "poor." The Italian *ä* as in "arm" gives difficulty to some children, as they tend to give a short *ă* in place of it or to use the muscles in a lax, indefinite way. Since this latter sound gives a good deal of difficulty to adults on the stage and in the opera, it is not surprising that children should find it difficult. It requires definite tension to flatten the tongue front and back and to secure a resonant, euphonious sound. We tell the children that they must try to "let the tongue lie like a rug on the floor of the mouth." Since *ä* is one of the low-frequency vowels, some children do not hear it well.[11]

The vowels *ō* (as in "tone"), *ōō* (as in "tool"), and *ē* (as in "beet"), together with the Italian *ä* (as in "arm"), seem to be the most difficult vowels and those on which we find the largest number of errors. The first three of these vowels, *ō*, *ōō*, and *ē*, are the lowest in frequencies of any of the vowel sounds, and speech difficulty with these sounds is undoubtedly due in many instances to hearing deficiency. Their characteristic frequencies begin as low as 375 cycles per second (for *ē* as in "team"), at 400 cycles per second (for *ōō* as in "pool"), and at 500 cycles for *ō* (as in "tone"), although they contain some higher components.

[11] H. Fletcher, *op. cit.*, p. 27.

SUMMARY

1. The home bears the chief responsibility for the appearance of many undesirable habits in speech.

2. There is need for analytical study of the results of speech tests on children.

3. Speech conditioning accounts for much delayed speech development.

4. Normal speech should be the aim of every parent; delayed speech may be due to psychological causes in children who are entirely normal on the physical side.

5. Our results of tests show the speech status of several groups of nursery-school children.

6. Much the same errors appear in all three groups.

7. Improvement on speech scores is found, following speech training.

8. Erroneous sounds are tabulated in order of frequency of occurrence.

9. Audiometer tests indicate that children with delayed or defective speech often score lower on audition than children with normal or superior speech.

10. Reduced auditory acuity is directly related to defective speech.

11. The child with delayed or defective speech may become psychoneurotic or psychotic if neglected at the time when speech readiness is present but unable to function.

12. The child with other handicaps as well as a speech defect is especially unfortunate, as the double handicap adds to his difficulty in adjustment and in making educational progress. There is need for individual speech training for children who are visually handicapped, deafened, or crippled. The major handicap is a serious burden. Minor defects such as speech or personality difficulties are remediable and should be treated as such, for the child's own advantage.

13. Untreated speech defects in childhood leave severe psychic scars in adulthood.

CHAPTER EIGHTEEN

THE BLIND CHILD AND HIS SPEECH

With the country's rapid increase in population, there is a considerable group of preschool blind children, who formerly were not considered eligible for a state school or public school before the ages of five to seven years. While some children are ready for private or public nursery schools earlier, there are few states which offer preschool training for the very young blind child. Where the home situation is favorable, the child is usually cared for in the home until able to enter the special school or special class. However, we have found many homes to be unsuitable for the care and education of the little blind child, as they lack the educational materials and backgrounds of experience and knowledge for the care of a handicapped child, even though they may do a very good job with seeing children in the same family. The severe critics of the residential school are usually those who do not understand the school's methods or its language.

SPEECH AND MENTAL TESTS

For a number of years the writer has given speech and mental tests as psychologist and speech consultant at the Nursery School for the Visually Handicapped Child, in Los Angeles. Results have demonstrated the value of early training of the preschool-aged blind child. The social development and maturation of personality seems to proceed much more rapidly when the child is stimulated by other children, in the nursery-school situation, than when he remains in the home, after the age of about two-and-a-half to three years. Tests of young children who are blind must be given by substituting the auditory and kinesthetic areas for the visual, unless there is some vision present. Baby tests such as the Gesell, the Psyche Cattell, Kuhlman, Buehler, and others are given to determine the mental age at entrance to the school. The Blanton-Stinchfield speech tests are given to those whose speech is inadequate, absent, or retarded, as is often the case. We often use a "treasure box" of toys representing all the sounds of English, substituting other stimuli when necessary, if the child does not know the object.

Speech.—Fifty-three nursery-school blind children were studied, as to speech at entrance. Of these, twenty-one were boys and thirty-two were girls, a ratio of two boys to three girls. They were found to have speech defects varying from no speech at all, to lisping, letter substitutions, or other inaccuracies. Usually there are more boys than girls among those having defects of speech, but in this case there were more girls than boys in the school. Table VI shows the results of the speech tests.

It will be seen that delayed speech and absence of speech far out-

155

TABLE VI

Types of Speech Defects

	Boys	Girls	Total	Percent of Total	
Delayed speech	3	4	7	13	
Dyslalia (lisping)	3	2	5	9	
Dyslalia and letter substitution ..	1	3	4	8	
Echolalia	2	1	3	6	
Foreign accent	1	1	2	4	(bilingual)
Infantile perseveration	1	4	5	9	
Lisping and stuttering	1	0	1	2	
Spastic and delayed speech	0	1	1	2	
No speech at entrance	4	4	8	15	
Normal speech at entrance	4	11	15	28	
Very superior vocabulary	1	1	2	4	
	21	32	53	100	

numbered all other types of speech difficulty. While we may observe that about one fourth (28 percent) possessed normal speech, almost as many had no speech at all, and the balance (over 50 percent) had delayed or defective speech. To the child and his parents this is important—educationally, socially, and emotionally. Recognizing this, the Nursery School arranged for a teacher to be trained in the moto-kinesthetic method, and to work with the children in need of speech re-education or speech training. A very few of these children possessed superior vocabularies at entrance, and these were children from superior family backgrounds and with superior intelligence. The results show that there was a much higher percentage of speech defects among this group of nursery-school-aged children than we would find in an unselected group of children in regular day-nursery schools.

Mental Tests.—The mental tests showed that, although the girls were slightly older chronologically, the boys had a higher mental age and a higher average I.Q. than the girls. The difference cannot be due to the larger number of girls, as the actual age was very nearly the same for the boys as for the girls tested.

We have found considerable advancement in intelligence quotients of children who have remained in the school long enough to be retested after their speech has developed; they have become adjusted, and many of them are now in the classes for visually handicapped in public schools.[1]

Gesell has recently pointed out the great importance of vision to the child's normal development. Lack of experiences common to the seeing child may lead to mental and physical retardation in the case of the sightless child.[2]

[1] S. P. Hayes, *First Regional Conference on Mental Measurements of the Blind,* (Watertown, Mass.: Perkins Institution, 1952).

[2] A. Gesell, *Vision* (New York: P. Hoeber Co., 1949).

Blindisms.—In addition to mannerisms, or so-called "blindisms," such as facial grimaces, tics or habit movements, restless motions of the body and lower extremities, we often find repetition of words and phrases, without meaning to the child, but in imitation of others.[3] Like the deaf child, the blind lack the type of thinking which comes easily to the seeing child, as they have not had the necessary experiences. With the increase in the case load in schools for the blind, as well as in the more recently developed special classes for the blind in public schools, teachers and heads of institutions feel that a remedial handicap, such as a speech defect, should be dealt with as soon as possible in the child's early growth period. The larger schools for the blind maintain a teacher of speech correction, as well as a teacher of speech arts.

Nursery-school training.—Realizing the lack of facilities for the care of the preschool-aged blind child, the nursery school to which we have already referred opened a modest day school in Los Angeles more than fifteen years ago. It was sponsored by alumnae of Delta Gamma National Sorority, who have recently built a larger home to accommodate twenty-five resident pupils and some day pupils, on a twenty-four-hour schedule, five days a week, enabling the children to keep in touch with their families by home visits each week end.

Dr. Lillian Titcomb, one of the founders, has arranged for a parental guidance program, and consultations are given to parents of children too young to enter a school, but who need home guidance or direction. This is known as the Cradle Roll or Cradle Club group.[4]

Speech training.—Training children to express their wants goes along with fundamentals of muscular development, self-feeding, dressing, and bathroom hygiene. The parents within the home seem unable to train their blind offspring in many of these performances. It is important that it be accomplished, however, before the child enters the nursery school, in order to free the time of nurses, attendants, and teachers for training along more important lines, and enabling the child more nearly to keep pace with the average child of his age.

Lacking the visual stimulation of watching facial expression and muscle movements of the speaker, the blind child must get her cues through sound and touch. The school has found that the moto-kinesthetic stimulation for speech saves time and helps the child to gain more accurate speech patterns with the least loss of time.

The blind want to be accepted by seeing persons and to take responsibility. Speech is therefore one of their most important tools. A speech defect acts as a social and an economic barrier to one already sufficiently handicapped. For this reason, schools for the blind are paying more and more attention to the development of speech and personality, along with

[3] W. C. Olson, *Child Development* (Boston: D. C. Heath & Co., 1949), p. 263 ff.
[4] L. R. Titcomb, "Why and How We Teach Parents of Blind Babies," *Medical Women's Journal*, January 1951.

the acquisition of more formal education and some degree of manual skill.[5]

In surveys made by the writer several years ago in the Overbrook School for the Blind in Pennsylvania and at Perkins Institution for the Blind in Massachusetts, many children were found to have speech defects ranging from letter substitutions and lisping to severe stuttering. There was a higher percentage of speech defects in these special schools than one finds in an unselected group of public-school children.[6]

Children originally thought to be retarded in speech and mental acumen often advance surprisingly during two or three years of nursery-school training. One of the most remarkable was Jan, at the Nursery School for the Visually Handicapped in Los Angeles, who had a decided lisp when he entered the school. Born prematurely, he was incubated for some weeks, then breast-fed to the ninth month. His blindness was due to retrolental fibroplasia in one eye, and to glaucoma in the other. When he was six months old the parents were told at the hospital that he would probably be mentally deficient. Alarmed, the parents at once consulted an ophthalmologist, and this early contact and subsequent advice may have had much to do with the fact that the boy proved later on to be far from mentally deficient, being classed as superior when he entered the Nursery School, and really considered to be a near-genius, with an intelligence quotient of 151. His lisp was doubtless caused by thumb-sucking, as he had an overbite when we first saw him. All of his *s* and *z* sounds and their blends were blurred or lisped and indistinct.

He was given speech training which stressed the moto-kinesthetic method, the teacher showing him the correct speech patterns and helping him to produce the sounds as well as to close the teeth and to make the correct tongue movements, so that at length he was able to make the necessary compensatory movements himself, unaided, and to entirely eliminate his lisp. He possessed a remarkable vocabulary and expressed himself with ease and fluency.

Several children, who were speechless at the time when they entered the nursery school, received speech training through the direction of the speech muscles by the teacher, as already described in Part I of this book. The stimulus also of hearing other children talk and of being stimulated socially helped them to overcome their tendency to withdraw, and to enter fully into the social life of the school.

THE CRADLE CLUB

The Cradle Club is a special group, composed of children whose names are on the waiting list for the Nursery School for the Visually Handicapped of Los Angeles. It was organized because of the school's experi-

---

[5] S. M. Stinchfield and E. H. Young, *op. cit.*

[6] S. M. Stinchfield, *The Speech of the Blind* (Proc. Biennial Conf.) (Nashville, Tenn.: Teachers of the Blind, 1926).

ence with many children from three to six years of age, who at entrance had had no adequate training in the home during babyhood. While physical care and attention had been given, some of these children had been pampered and spoiled. Habits were infantile and toilet training had not been given; some could not chew or even bite a cracker. Food was sometimes sucked from a bottle with an enlarged hole in the nipple, and many times the diet was inadequate. Many such children did not talk, but made their wants known by whining, crying, or by temper tantrums. The school learned early in its existence that it was far more advantageous to train the infant during the early months in the home, before he entered the nursery school, than to have to train a neglected child after he entered the school.

The training of mothers in the Cradle Roll group has been found especially important in dealing with the retrolental fibroplasia cases; these seem to be on the increase in schools for the blind, because the obstetrician and the pediatrician are now very successful in saving babies that formerly died soon after birth.

In our experience, wherever the mothers of these cases have received adequate help while the child was too young to enter a nursery school, it has been found that the children respond rapidly and well, and eliminate hours of patient training by workers in the school.[7] Teachers may even proceed along the usual line, educationally, once the child enters the school, rather than having to wait for him to catch up, while learning the fundamentals of living, which should have been taught in the home before the child was placed in any school.

If, by a little timely help, we may enable the very young child to become better socialized through speech and knowledge of essentials—through training, play, advice to the mothers, and the like—it will save many hours for both teacher and pupil, once he enters the school.[8]

SPEECH OF THE DEAF AND THE DEAF-BLIND CHILD

A teacher who has used the moto-kinesthetic method for three years in a large state school for the deaf with deaf-blind beginning pupils, also applied this type of training in 1951–52 with a class of nine deaf children who had had some training by the older methods.[9] They were taught by a combination of the moto-kinesthetic and vibration methods, with rewarding results. Hearing loss ranged from total, congenital deafness to about fifty decibels in the speech range. There was not any appreciable difference in fluency of speech and articulation of specific sounds, after

[7] K. E. Maxfield, "The Pre-School Blind Child. A Preliminary Study," *Teachers Forum*, VI (1934), 62–65.

[8] F. M. Stevens, "Our Baby Was Born Blind," *Saturday Evening Post*, December 27, 1952, pp. 16–18 and 46–47.

[9] Personal communication from Miss Mabel Talbot, teacher in the Iowa State School for the Deaf (Council Bluffs, Iowa, February 1954).

use of the method, as between the very deaf child and the one with the most hearing. Inflection and tonal quality varied, of course, in accordance with amounts of residual hearing. The vibration technique was valuable for development of pleasing voices in the profoundly deaf members of the class.

The main results were that the children learned the moto-kinesthetic method quickly, and were soon able to imitate new words with the aid of the stimulation given by the teacher, and they could and did use spoken language freely. It was very encouraging to get such results from a second-year class, eight of whom entered the school without language. The ninth child was a transfer from public school, and the method was used for speech correction in her case, the results coming quite rapidly.

The moto-kinesthetic method, according to Miss Talbot, is effective with the slowest children who have difficulty in understanding the usual techniques, and is much more effective with the brighter children. Moreover, the difficult double- and triple-consonant combinations, such as *tr*, *cl*, *sl*, to name only three, are not difficult when the appropriate double stimulation is used. She used the moto-kinesthetic method for *teaching speech*—which is a more difficult process than *speech correction*. While this teacher's work is now entirely with the deaf-blind, she reports that were she again to teach those who are merely deaf, it would be done with the stimulative technique as the principal teaching method. In working with the deaf-blind she uses the moto-kinesthetic method exclusively, for teaching speech. Using this method, all of the children have begun to say a few words, although they had not responded to other methods used previously. Two new pupils, a girl and a boy, who entered the school this year, and who seem to be considerably above average in intelligence, have begun speech work and are progressing rapidly. The boy already uses several short sentences and the girl uses several words. Because of the language barrier operative in the field of the deaf, these children must be taught *ideas* before they are taught *words*. The higher the intelligence quotient the quicker the child absorbs ideas and the sooner he is ready for speech. With children who are only average, the idea-teaching is slower, hence speech is delayed. Even though not ready for language, the latter children are quite adept at following stimulation, at practising sequences, and at drilling on syllables. One child who is totally deaf, and with only shadow perception in vision, is able to say any word or sentence the teacher may direct. Working with these children she has found that the stimulative technique is the quickest and surest way to establish the idea of speech, whereas previously teachers had not been able to reach these pupils through the usual techniques to which the teachers had been accustomed.

The lip reading of an experimental group, using the moto-kinesthetic and vibration stimulation, improved from poor or average to superior. Speech obtained by smooth, quick stimulation was easy, and rapid and natural in sound. It was less of a strain upon the pupils, since it reduced the demand upon their vision and allowed them to work in more relaxed fashion. Its effectiveness—especially with pupils who were not yet good at analytical thinking—could not be overemphasized. For those pupils who were analytical, it provided a means of speeding up articulation and preventing jerky speech.

In describing their work to the author, many teachers have said that there is no doubt that the moto-kinesthetic technique offers invaluable help in speech development and in speech correction, and they regret not having come in contact with the method earlier in their careers.

Finally, we may say that direction by the adult helps the pupil to feel, as well as to form, the correct movements, and later to recall them through kinesthetic impressions. It gives him something definite and specific to do about his speech defect, something he learns to do first under direction, and then by himself. The golden age for corrective speech training seems to us to be at the time when the child shows the desire and need to express himself—somewhere between the end of the first year and the beginning of the third year. Correction is made then easily and quickly, whereas if postponed until he is ready for school or thereabouts, the difficulty of transforming his speech is doubled and he may turn against all efforts to try to talk.[10]

[10] S. S. Hawk, "Moto-Kinaesthetic Training for Children with Speech Handicaps," *Journal of Speech Disorders*, VII, No. 4 (December 1942), 357–60.

CHAPTER NINETEEN

SPEECH AND INTELLIGENCE OF THE MENTALLY DEFICIENT CHILD

CAUSES OF RETARDATION

Surveys show that about 5 percent of all children are exceptionally dull or mentally deficient. Many states require that a child who is two or more years retarded in school shall be placed in a special class for backward children in the school system.

Delayed speech development does not necessarily mean that a child is mentally deficient. There are many other causes of slow development, such as deafness or hearing loss, childhood illnesses, unfavorable environment, intense emotional disturbances, or other complex factors which retard speech and mental growth.

The duller the child, the less responsive he seems to be to speech stimuli. The moron is imitative, possesses a fair vocabularly, may be trained to do many useful things, and often passes for normal. The imbecile may imitate sounds fairly well and have quite a vocabulary of the concrete type, but he tends to slur word endings, to omit middle and final consonants, and often lapses after months of speech training. The idiot has few if any words and may be utterly incapable of acquiring intelligible speech at all.[1]

Feeling that the speech specialist and psychologist should not abandon the effort to help the backward child educationally and socially, for his own sake and for that of his family, as well as for society, the writer undertook to do mental testing and some remedial work with children in an independent school for mentally deficient children, in northern California. The work has continued for several years in this school, which houses about seventy-five resident pupils and provides a large staff of housemothers and routine workers, and teachers for the various mental-aged groups from kindergarten to higher elementary level.[2]

SPEECH AND MENTAL TESTS

Periodic tests for speech and intelligence over a ten-year period, through semiannual visits to the school by the writer, have revealed certain facts about the mentally deficient child and his possibilities for speech development which we believe to be important in estimating the time required for the educational and speech development to become effective.

[1] H. Ashby, "Speech Defects in Mentally Deficient Children," *Medical Chronicles* (October 1903).
[2] The Cedars Development School at Ross, Marin County, California.

As this work will be described in a longer article elsewhere, we shall merely summarize the results of our study rather briefly.[3]

We found, for instance, that the sounds on which our subjects had the most difficulty, and on which the highest percentage of errors occurred, were the high-frequency sounds *s*, *z*, *sh*, *zh*, *ch*, *j*, and *th*, as well as on the sounds of *l* and *r* and blends containing the foregoing sounds such as *sl*, *sp*, *sk*, *pl*, *gl*, *fr*, *gr*, *tr*, etc. Our earlier studies of normal nursery-school children and those learning to talk showed that these were also the most difficult sounds for children in those groups. Moreover, these sounds seem to be technically more difficult for most children than the more primitive consonants, namely the labials *p*, *b*, and *m*, tip-of-tongue sounds *t*, *d*, and *n*, back-of-tongue sounds *k*, *g*, and *ng* and semivowels *w*, *wh*, *h*, and *y*. These primitive consonants, so called, seem to be more easily observed, visually, than the high-frequency sounds, which are made somewhat farther back in the mouth, and less clearly detected from an auditory standpoint than the lower frequency sounds.

In addition to the above we have found that certain sounds present difficulty; the following common errors and substitutions are made:

sh for *s* (shoap for soap)	*d* for *th* (fedder for feather)
s for *th* (simble for thimble)	*d* for *g* (dirl for girl)
th for *z* (thebra for zebra)	*k* for *g* (coat for goat)
th for *f* (thoot for foot)	*s* omitted ('poon for spoon)
h for *c* (k) (how for cow)	*t* for *th* (ting for thing)
f and *v* for voiced and voiceless *th* (vis for this) (fum for thumb)	*p* for *k* (pup for cup)
w for *r* and *l* (wed for red; wight for light)	

Among blends on which errors seemed to be most frequent were:

b for *bl* (b'ock for block)	*f* for *fl* (f'ower for flower)
dr for *gr* (dreen for green)	*gw* for *gr* (gwapes for grapes)
bw for *br* (bwed for bread)	*kw* for *kl* (kwock for clock)

Similar errors or substitutions often occur on blends containing *s* and *z*, such as *st*, *sp*, *sl*, *gz*, *lz*, *vz*, etc.

Speech tests given to fifty-three subjects, boys and girls, revealed the types of speech defects shown in Table VII, which summarizes the speech defects found in all subjects tested, boys and girls, at Cedars Development School in California.

A considerable number were speechless at the time they entered the school. Oral inaccuracies, letter substitutions, and lisping came next.

Medians obtained from the speech tests, boys and girls.—The Blanton-

---

[3] To appear in a subsequent issue of the *Journal of Speech Disorders*, as "Speech Prediction in the Mentally Deficient Child."

TABLE VII

SPEECH DEFECTS IN CHILDREN

Type of speech defect	Percentage of cases
Oral inaccuracies	16
Letter substitutions	13
Lisping on *s* and *z* sounds	11
Lisping on *s* and *z* blends only	7
High-frequency sounds and *l* and *r* blends	5
Spastic speech	5
Lisping and omission of mid- and final consonants	5
Babbling only (inarticulate speech)	4
s and *z* sounds; substitution of *f* and *v* for voiced and voiceless *th* and blends	4
Stuttering	2
Omitting many mid- and final consonants	2
Chief difficulty on *l* and *r* blends	2
Nasality	2
Dyslexia and dyslalia	2
Entirely speechless	18

Stinchfield speech tests were used to test the speech of these children. The tests contain all of the initial, middle, and final consonants.[4] The median score for girls, thirty-three in number, was 50 out of a possible score of 100. The median score for boys, fifty-five in all, was 66. The boys were thus slightly better than the girls.

Mental tests. — Fifty-nine subjects were given the Stanford-Binet, 1937 Revision, Form L. On this the boys made a higher score than the girls on mental age and intelligence quotients, even though the boys averaged slightly younger than the girls, chronologically.

SPEECH AND INTELLIGENCE

Studies have been made by several writers within the past half-century, showing the relationship between speech proficiency and intelligence. In our study we found that intelligence quotients correlated slightly higher with speech score than did mental age, although there was a positive plus correlation between speech and mental age. Moreover we found a low but positive plus correlation between chronological age and speech. This seems to indicate that the higher the mental age and intelligence quotient of the individual, the greater are his chances for speech development.[5]

Speech training.—The moto-kinesthetic method of speech training has been found the most useful and effective, by the various speech teachers at Cedars Development School, as it quickly demonstrates to the child

[4] *Blanton-Stinchfield Speech Tests and Measurements.*

[5] J. Bangs, "A Clinical Analysis of the Articulatory Defects of the Feeble-Minded," *Journal of Speech Disorders* (Iowa City, Ia.), December 1942, pp. 343–56.

how his errors may be corrected, not only through hearing the sound and seeing the teacher's face as she says the various words, but in gaining firsthand knowledge of the movements through stimulation given by the teacher, so that he soon learns to follow the sound sequence through the entire word in normal timing, without omissions, because he knows how it feels and, as time goes on, knows how to correct it himself.

The child with acute hearing progresses usually more rapidly than the child who is slow of comprehension and who lacks auditory acuity. It is therefore logical that we should employ the motor help needed to show the child just where, how, and when to form the sound, so as to produce it by himself, after a time, when he will need no further aid. This requires special training on the part of the teacher, as acquiring skill in teaching this method is much like acquiring skill in using a new and unknown musical instrument, except that the teacher already "knows the score" and, with her phonetic knowledge, is able with some practice to acquire the skill needed for teaching the child just how to form the words needed for his ordinary everyday uses. Once he has gained this skill, his entire personality and his social outlook and adjustment improve immeasurably.

Not only is the speech improved, but over a period of years we have found that once the child acquires speech, he gains in comprehension, language understanding, insight into verbal concepts, and into meaning of numbers; and his whole mental horizon is enlarged, even though he may never progress as far as the child of average intelligence. That he is more acceptable to his parents is shown by the increasing frequency of home visits, and the pleasure reported by parents in the improved power of communication which the child has acquired through special speech training.[6]

The kinesthetic areas in the brain seem unimpaired in many cases of mental deficiency. A child may acquire speech in such cases through moto-kinesthetic stimulation, learning to associate ideas with the sounds and movements. He then builds up a vocabulary and is able to talk about things of a concrete nature and of common interest in his daily life, and thus he becomes happier because of his improved social status in his contacts with other children and adults.[7]

Illustrations.—We have had the experience of working with a mongoloid child of four years, who was speechless at the time he began his lessons. He improved rapidly through the application of the method of stimulation which we have described, and at the close of eighteen months of training he was able to communicate sufficiently to make his wants known and to express the ordinary desires incident to his daily life, even though limited mentally and physically. By use of articulate speech, emo-

[6] H. J. Baker, *Characteristic Differences in Bright and Dull Pupils* (Bloomington, Ill.: Public School Publishing Company, 1927).

[7] H. J. Baker, *Introduction to Exceptional Children* (New York: The Macmillan Company, 1947).

tional tension was lessened and a quieter, happier existence was the result.

Another mongoloid child was referred to the writer at the Casa Colina Convalescent Hospital for Crippled Children at Chino, California, about a year ago. This child had only a few monosyllables and meaningless jargon when he entered the hospital, following surgery. With moto-kinesthetic speech training once a week and some follow-up work by nurses, this child began to use words and then short sentences, until at the end of nine months, before he was sent home, he was talking with less difficulty, making himself clearly understood, and showing more understanding and intelligence than had been thought possible, originally. We have the impression, based upon some years of experience with these and other speech patients, that some children have been diagnosed as mentally deficient when they really are retarded through adventitious conditions and are not congenitally mentally retarded. Early speech training may in such cases overcome the effects of the early slow development.[8]

Not only is the child happier, who learns to talk, because he now finds himself able to mingle freely with other children, but it is a source of great satisfaction to the parents and other relatives of such a child. For now, even though he may never equal the child of average or superior intelligence in understanding or in accomplishment, he can make his wants known and will show better comprehension and social understanding.

[8] A. and S. T. Binet, *Mentally Defective Children* (New York: Longmans, Green & Co., 1914).

REFERENCES

CHAPTERS I–VII

Gray, G. W., and C. M. Wise. *The Bases of Speech*. New York: Harper & Brothers, 1946.

CHAPTER VIII

Beatty, H. G. "Etiology of Cleft Palate and Hare Lip," *Journal of Speech Disorders*, I (1936), 13–20.

Blair, V. P. "Cleft Palate—Its Surgery," *Journal of Speech Disorders*, II (1937), 195–98.

Brown, J. B. "Elongation of the Cleft Palate to Gain Better Nasopharyngeal Closure," *Proceedings of 'the American Speech Correction Association*, IX (1939), 21–25.

Cobb, L. H., and D. Lierle. "An Analysis of Speech Difficulties of 56 Cleft Palate and Harelip Cases," *Archives of Speech*, I (1936), 217–30.

Dorrance, G. M. "Congenital Insufficiency of the Palate," *Archives of Surgery*, XXI (1930), 185–248.

———. "The Push-Back Operation in Cleft Palate Surgery," *Annals of Surgery*, CI (No. 1, 1935), 445–60.

Fitz-Gibbon, J. "Cleft Palate," *Proceedings of the American Speech Correction Association*, IV (1934), 52–55.

Harkins, C. S. "Rehabilitation of the Cleft Palate Child," *Journal of the Exceptional Child*, IX (1943), 98–106.

Harrington, R. "A Study of the Mechanism of Velopharyngeal Closure," *Journal of Speech Disorders*, IX (1944), 325–45.

Hawk, Sara Stinchfield. *Speech Therapy for the Physically Handicapped*. Stanford, Calif.: Stanford University Press, 1950.

Kantner, C. E. "Four Devices Used in the Treatment of Rhinolalia Aperta," *Journal of Speech Disorders*, II (1937), 73–76.

Koepp-Baker, H. "Some Anatomic and Physiologic Considerations in Uraniscolalia," *Proceedings of the American Speech Correction Association*, VIII (1938), 84–86.

Ward, W. K. "Re-educating Cleft Palate Speech," *The Practitioner*, CXXIII (1929), 148–52.

West, R., and others. *The Rehabilitation of Speech*. New York: Harper & Brothers, 1937, pp. 65–86, 268–75.

Young, E. H. *Overcoming Cleft Palate Speech*. Minneapolis: Hill-Young School, 1928.

CHAPTER IX–X

Hughes, Carol. "Canada's Mother of Courage," *Coronet* (August 1949), pp. 97–100.

CHAPTER XI

Barrows, S. T., and K. Hall. *Games and Jingles for Speech Training.* Boston: Expression Co., 1936.

Bender, J. F., and V. Fields. *Principles and Practices of Speech Correction.* New York: Pitman Press, n.d.

Carlson, E. *Born That Way.* New York: John Day Co., 1941.

Cass, M. T. *Speech Habilitation in Cerebral Palsy.* New York: Columbia University Press, 1951.

Davidson, L. D. "Methods for Treatment of Disorders of Speech Due to Birth Injury," *Quarterly Journal of Speech,* XXII (October 1936), 404.

Fairbanks, G. *Voice and Articulation Drillbook.* New York: Harper & Brothers, 1940.

Fröschels, E. *Psychological Elements in Speech.* Boston: Expression Co., 1932.

———. *Speech Therapy.* Boston: Expression Co., 1933.

Garrison, K. C. *The Psychology of Exceptional Children.* (Part VI, "Emotionally and Socially Maladjusted Children.") Rev. ed. New York: Ronald Press, 1950.

Gifford, M. F. *Nervous Speech Disorders.* New York: Prentice-Hall Co., 1939.

Gratke, J. M. *Help Them Help Themselves.* Dallas: Texas Society for Crippled Children, 1947.

Hawk, Sara S. *Speech Therapy for the Physically Handicapped.* Stanford, Calif.: Stanford University Press, 1950.

Irwin, R. B. "Speech Comes to a Five-Year-Old Boy," *Journal of Speech Disorders,* XI (September 1946), 197–203.

Johnson, W., *et al. Speech Handicapped School Children.* New York: Harper & Brothers, 1948.

Lord, E. E. *Children Handicapped by Cerebral Palsy.* New York: Commonwealth Fund, 1937.

———. *Development of Children with Lesions in the Central Nervous System.* Yale Psycho-Clinic, Genetic Psychology Monographs, No. 7, 1930.

Murray, Elwood. *The Speech Personality.* 2d rev. ed. Philadelphia: J. B. Lippincott Co., 1944.

Phelps, W. M. "The Care and Treatment of Cerebral Palsied," *Journal of the American Medical Association,* III (July 2, 1938), 1–6.

Robbins, S. D. *Dictionary of Terms Dealing with Defective Speech.* Cambridge, Mass.: Sci-Art Publishers, 1951.

Robbins, S. D., and R. Robbins. *Corrections of Speech Defects of Early Childhood.* Boston: Expression Co., 1937.

Rogers, G., and L. D. Thomas. *New Pathways for Children with Cerebral Palsy.* New York: The Macmillan Co., 1935.

Rutherford, B. R. *Give Them a Chance to Talk.* Minneapolis: Burgess Publishing Co., 1948.

Scheidemann, N. *The Psychology of Exceptional Children.* ("Major and Minor Speech Defects," "Word Blindness," "Left-Handedness," Vol. I.) Boston: Houghton Mifflin Co., 1931.

Seth, George, and D. J. Guthrie. *Speech in Childhood.* New York: Oxford University Press, 1935.

Stinchfield, S. M. *Handy-Pack Speech Cards. An Articulation Test for All the Sounds of English, with Pictures.* Chicago: C. H. Stoelting Co., 1940.

Stoddard, C. B. *Sounds for Little Folks.* Boston: Expression Co., 1940.

Van Riper, Charles. *Speech Correction.* New York: Prentice-Hall Co., 1939.

Weiss, D. A. "Speech in Retarded Children," *The Nervous Child*, IX, No. 1 (1951), 21–30.

West, Robert, and others. *The Rehabilitation of Speech.* Rev. ed. New York: Harper & Brothers, 1947.

[Authors' note: Miscellaneous publications on cerebral palsy may be obtained from the National Society of Crippled Children and Adults, 11 So. LaSalle St., Chicago 3, Ill.]

CHAPTER XII

Bastian, H. D. *Aphasia and Other Speech Defects.* London: H. K. Lewis, 1898.

Desjerine, J. "Etude sur l' Aphasie," Revue du Monde, V (1885), 174–91.

Ewing, A. W. *Aphasia in Children.* New York: Oxford University Press, 1930.

Franz, S. I. "The Relations of Aphasia," *Journal of General Psychology*, III (1930), 401–11.

Goldstein, Kurt. *Language and Language Disturbances.* New York: Grune and Stratton, 1948.

Head, Henry. *Aphasia and Kindred Disorders of Speech.* 2 vols. New York: The Macmillan Co., 1926.

Hoffman, J. A. "Training of Children with Aphasic Understanding," *The Nervous Child*, IX, No. 1 (1951), 85–88.

Howe, H. S. "Cortical Word Blindness," *Neurological Bulletin*, III (1921), 64–71.

Marie, Pierre, and C. Foix. "Les Aphasies de Guerre," *Revue générale de clinique et thérapeutique*, XXXI (1917), 451–54.

Meyer, A. *The Present State of Aphasia and Apraxia.* (Harvey Lectures, 1909–10, No. 5.) Philadelphia: J. B. Lippincott Co., 1910.

Monroe, Marion. *Children Who Cannot Read.* Rev. ed. Chicago: University of Chicago Press, 1934.

Nielsen, J. M. *Agnosia, Apraxia, and Aphasia.* Los Angeles: Neurological Society of Los Angeles, 1936. New York: P. Hoeber Co., 1947.

Orton, S. T. "Some Studies in the Language Function," *Publication of the Association for Research in Nervous and Mental Diseases*, XIII (1933), 614–33.

Osnato, M. *Aphasia and Associated Speech Problems.* New York: P. Hoeber Co., 1920.

Stinchfield, S. M. *Speech Disorders.* New York: Harcourt, Brace & Co., 1933.

Stinchfield, S. M., and E. H. Young. *Children with Delayed and Defective Speech.* Stanford, Calif.: Stanford University Press, 1938.

Wallin, J. *Children with Mental and Physical Handicaps.* New York: Prentice-Hall Co., 1949.

Weisenburg, Theodore H., and K. E. McBride. *Aphasia.* New York: Commonwealth Fund, 1935.

Wilson, S. A. K. *Aphasia.* London: Kegan Paul, 1926.

Yearsley, M. "Congenital Deficiency of Speech Areas; Congenital Aphasia," *British Medical Journal,* II (1911), 248.

CHAPTERS XIII–XIV

Van Riper, Charles. *Stuttering.* Prepared for the American Speech and Hearing Association under the editorship of Wendell Johnson, 1948.

CHAPTER XV

Allport, Gordon. *Social Psychology.* Boston: Houghton Mifflin Co., 1924.

Barrows, S. T., and K. Hall. *Games and Jingles for Speech Training.* Boston: Expression Co., 1936.

Bluemel, C. S. *Stammering and Allied Disorders.* New York: The Macmillan Co., 1936.

Broca, P. "Sur la siège de la faculté de 'langage articule' avec deux observations d'aphémie," *Bulletin de la société Anatomique de Paris,* August 1861.

Ewing, A. W. *Aphasia in Children.* London: Oxford Medical Publications, 1930.

Fröschels, E. *Psychological Elements in Speech.* Boston: Expression Co., 1932.

Goldstein, K. "Die transkortikalen Aphasien," *Deutsche Zeitschrift für Nervenh.,* LII (1914), 504–14.

Hawk, S. S. *Speech Therapy for the Physically Handicapped Child.* Stanford, Calif.: Stanford University Press, 1950.

Head, Henry. *Aphasia and Kindred Disorders of Speech.* Vol. I. New York: The Macmillan Co., 1936.

Hinshelwood, J. "Congenital Word-Blindness," *Lancet,* Vol. LXXVII (1900).

Lord, E. E. *Children Handicapped by Cerebral Palsy.* New York: Commonwealth Fund, 1937.

McGraw, M. *Growth.* New York: Appleton-Century Co., 1935.

Marie, Pierre. "Revision de la question de l'aphasie," *Semana Médica* (Buenos Aires), May 23, 1906.

Meumann, E. *Psychology of Learning.* New York: D. Appleton Co., 1913.

Monakow, C. von. *Gehirnpathologie.* 2d ed. Wien: A. Holder, 1905.

Monroe, Marion. "Suggestions for Remedial Reading." Pittsburgh, Pa. mimeo., n.d.

Monroe, Marion, and B. Backus. *Remedial Reading.* Boston: Houghton Mifflin Co., 1937.

Moutier, François. *L'Aphasie de Broca.* Paris: G. W. Steinheil, 1908.

Nielsen, J. M. *Agnosia, Apraxia, and Aphasia.* Los Angeles: Neurological Society of Los Angeles, 1936.

Ogden, C. K., and I. A. Richards. *The Meaning of Meaning.* New York: Harcourt, Brace & Co., 1937.

Orton, S. T. *Reading, Writing, and Speech Problems in Children.* New York: W. W. Norton, 1937.

Piaget, Jean. *The Language and Thought of the Child.* New York: Harcourt, Brace & Co., 1926.

Pick, A. "Zur Frage nach der Natur der Echolalie," *Fortschritte der Psychologie,* Bd. 4, H. 1.

Robbins, Samuel D. *A Dictionary of Speech Pathology and Therapy.* Cambridge, Mass.: Sci-Art Publishers, 1951.

Rogers, G., and L. Thomas. *New Pathways for Children with Cerebral Palsy.* New York: The Macmillan Co., 1935.

Stern, Clara, and William Stern. *Kindersprache.* (Monographien über die seelische Entwicklung des Kindes. No. 1.) Leipzig: J. A. Barth, 1907.

Stern, W. *The Psychology of Early Childhood.* New York: Henry Holt & Co., 1930.

Stinchfield, S. M. *Handy-Pack Speech Cards. An Articulation Test for All the Sounds of English, with Pictures.* Chicago: C. H. Stoelting Co., 1937.

———. *Speech Disorders.* New York: Harcourt, Brace & Co., 1933.

CHAPTER XVI

Ayres Spelling Scale. Russell Sage Foundation, 1915.

Blanton-Stinchfield Speech Tests and Measurements. Chicago: C. H. Stoelting Co., 1923, 1937.

Durrell, D. D. *Analysis of Reading Difficulty.* Yonkers, N.Y.: World Book Co., 1937.

Fernald, G. M. *Remedial Techniques in Basic School Subjects.* New York: McGraw-Hill Book Co., Inc., 1943.

Garrett, H. E. *Statistics in Psychology and Education.* New York: Longmans, Green & Co., 1937.

Gates, A. *Round the World Reader.* Yonkers, N.Y.: World Book Co., 1930.

Gray, W. S. *Diagnostic Reading Tests.* Chicago: C. H. Stoelting Co., 1933.

Hincks, E. M. *Disability in Learning to Read in Relation to Neurosis.* Harvard Monographs in Education, Ser. 1, Vol. II, No. 2, 1926.

———. *Disability in Reading and Its Relation to Personality.* Harvard Graduate School of Education, 1926.

Lord, E. E., L. Carmichel, and W. F. Dearborn. *Special Disabilities in Learning to Read and Write.* Harvard Monographs in Education, Ser. 1, Vol. II, No. 1, June 1925.

Monroe, Marion. *Children Who Cannot Read.* Chicago: University of Chicago Press, 1932.

———. *Diagnostic Reading Examination.* Chicago: C. H. Stoelting Co., 1932.

Orton, S. T. *Development of Speech Understanding in Relation to Intelligence.* Vol. I, No. 6. Langhorne, Pa.: Child Research Clinic, Woods School, 1936.

———. "Familiar Occurrence of Disorders in Acquisition of Language," *Eugenics,* III (April 1930), 4.

———. "Special Disability in Spelling," *Bulletin of the Neurological Institute* (New York), June 1931.

Travis, L. E. *Speech Pathology.* New York: D. Appleton Co., 1931.

CHAPTER XVII

Blanton-Stinchfield Speech Tests and Measurements. Chicago: C. H. Stoelting Co., 1923, 1937.

Crandall, I. B. *The Sounds of Speech.* (Tables taken from *Bell Telephone Laboratory Reprint B-162-1,* November 1925.) New York: Bell Telephone Company, 1925.

Ewing, A. W., and E. R. Ewing. *The Handicap of Deafness.* New York: Longmans, Green & Co., Inc., 1938.

Fletcher, H. *Speech and Hearing.* New York: D. Van Nostrand Co., 1929.

Nielsen, J. M. *Agnosia, Apraxia, and Aphasia.* Los Angeles: Neurological Society of Los Angeles, 1936.

Stinchfield, S. M. *Speech Disorders.* New York: Harcourt, Brace & Co., 1933.

CHAPTER XVIII

Gesell, A. *Vision.* New York: P. Hoeber Co., 1949.

Hawk, S. S. "Moto-Kinaesthetic Training for Children with Speech Handicaps," *Journal of Speech Disorders,* VII, No. 4 (December 1942), 357–60.

Hayes, S. P. *First Regional Conference on Mental Measurements of the Blind.* Watertown, Mass.: Perkins Institute, 1952.

Maxfield, K. E. "The Pre-School Blind Child. A Preliminary Study," *Teachers Forum,* VI (1934), 62–65.

Olson, W. C. *Child Development.* Boston: D. C. Heath & Co., 1949.

Stevens, F. M. "Our Baby Was Born Blind," *Saturday Evening Post,* December 27, 1952, pp. 16–18, 46–47.

Stinchfield, S. M. *The Speech of the Blind.* (Proc. Biennial Conf.) Nashville, Tenn.: Teachers of the Blind, 1926.

Stinchfield, S. M., and E. H. Young. *Children with Delayed or Defective Speech.* Stanford, Calif.: Stanford University Press, 1938.

Titcomb, L. R. "Why and How We Teach Parents of Blind Babies," *Medical Women's Journal,* LVIII, No. 1 (January 1951).

CHAPTER XIX

Ashby, H. "Speech Defects in Mentally Deficient Children," *Medical Chronicles,* October 1903.

Baker, H. J. *Characteristic Differences in Bright and Dull Pupils.* Bloomington, Ill.: Public School Publishing Co., 1927.

———. *Introduction to Exceptional Children.* New York: The Macmillan Co., 1927.

Bangs, J. "A Clinical Analysis of the Articulatory Defects of the Feeble-Minded," *Journal of Speech Disorders,* VII (December 1942), 343–56.

Binet, A., and S. T. Binet. *Mentally Defective Children.* New York: Longmans, Green & Co., 1914.

Blanton-Stinchfield Speech Tests and Measurements. Chicago: C. H. Stoelting Co., 1923, 1937.

Gesell, A. *The Retarded Child and How to Help Him.* Bloomington, Ill.: Public School Publishing Co., 1925.

Goddard, H. H. *The Kallikak Family.* Washington, D.C.: Nervous & Mental Diseases Publishing Co., 1912, 1919.

Hawk, S. S. "Speech Prediction in the Mentally Deficient Child," *Journal of Speech and Hearing Disorders,* to be published.

Miner, J. B. *Deficiency and Delinquency.* Baltimore: Warwick & York, 1918.

Scheidemann, N. *Psychology of Exceptional Children.* Boston: Houghton Mifflin Co., 1931 (Vol. I), 1937 (Vol. II).

Tredgold, A. F. *Mental Deficiency.* New York: Wm. Wood & Co., 1916.

Wallin, J. E. *Children with Mental and Physical Handicaps.* New York: Prentice-Hall Inc., 1949.

Wembridge, Eleanor. *Among the Low-Brows.* Boston: Houghton Mifflin Co., 1931.

INDEX